ORIGINS OF
THE UNIVERSE

INTERNATIONAL LIBRARY

ALBERT HINKELBEIN

ORIGINS OF
THE UNIVERSE

COLLINS · PUBLISHERS   FRANKLIN WATTS, INC.

London · Glasgow   New York

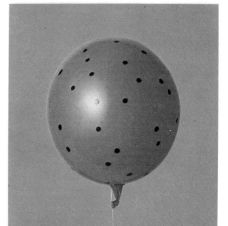

First Edition 1972

ISBN 0 00 100170 1 (*Collins*)
SBN 531 02112 2 (*Franklin Watts*)

CONTENTS

CHAPTER 1

IN THE
BEGINNING

No final answer

The mysteries surrounding the origins of the universe have occupied men's minds since history was first recorded—and probably longer. All the accounts which have been offered may well deal in concepts beyond our powers of imagination. But we are not content to have *no* explanation.

The course we shall follow here will be to examine some of the ideas about the universe which have been based on the observations that men have made. We shall seek to discover some of the laws which govern conditions in the universe and try to understand how they work. Only when this has been done will it be possible to evaluate the theories that have been proposed and decide which are acceptable and which are not.

We can start with the idea that many millions of years ago the world was created and then question the truth of this by searching for proof of the statement. We shall seek to show in later chapters that in the short term there *is* reason to believe that the world we know, Earth, was created at a specific point in time, and that it has not existed since the "beginning".

We must keep an open mind about the beginning. There are some who believe that our world came into existence with the creation of the solar system, the Sun and the planets and this is probably the correct view. The solar system, however, is but a very small part of the immense galaxy, the Milky Way, in which it is situated and that too must have been created at some point in time, but not necessarily at the same time as the solar system and Earth. Again, our galaxy is only one of countless similar collections of stars in space, not all of which were created at the same time, if one theory (the "steady state" theory) is to be believed. The evolution of our world and the solar system is probably on a different time scale from that of the galaxy, and the galaxy from the universe which is apparently limitless.

An expanding universe

There are two main theories about the origin of the universe. The first of these is the "big bang" theory which proposes that everything started from a vast primeval explosion of matter which scattered gas and dust throughout space. This process of dispersion is still going on and the scattered matter forms the galaxies and other cosmic bodies. The steady state theory proposes that matter, that is hydrogen gas, is being created continuously in intergalactic space. From this gas new concentrations of matter are being created in the form of galaxies to

The Great Nebula in Orion. The birth of stars.

Above: *A rugged alpine landscape. A young mountain range between thirty and sixty million years old.*

Right: *Young stars are big, often rotate quickly, generate a lot of energy and are extremely oblate.*

Below: *A white dwarf. The last stage in which a star can still be seen. It is very small and generates restricted energy.*

replace those that are disappearing with the expansion of the universe. The one feature common to both theories is that the universe is expanding.

Physical laws

There are views of the creation in which credit is given to God or gods. These views are not founded on scientific principles but on faith and they do not offer the sort of scientific proof we seek. Our approach, therefore, will be to examine the world we live in and the laws which govern it and the solar system, our part of space, and the galaxy to seek answers to the question of the origins of all that surrounds us.

The laws have been deduced from observations made of the physical conditions of Earth and are known only in terms of these conditions. They may not be the same as those throughout the universe, but they are an integral part of our world. Indeed they provide such a comprehensive and incontrovertible explanation of the conditions we observe that they must have been operative since its formation. No indication or evidence is to be found for assuming that they can ever have been different. It would be foolish to suggest that Earth came into existence contrary to its own laws.

Nevertheless, it should be remembered that in this type of discus-

A mature Black Forest landscape in Germany. An old mountain range formed about 300 million years ago.

A young spiral galaxy. Only a small amount of matter has condensed to form stars.

An old spiral galaxy. All the matter has condensed to form stars.

sion there are many areas of dispute and arguments are rife. The origin of the universe occurred so far back in time that the sequence of events is only dimly discernible.

Everything that decays with time must have originated once, that is everything that has an end must have had a beginning and we can cite examples. A burning candle which is consumed cannot have been burning indefinitely. Similarly, man is born, ages and dies. This is true not only of all life forms but also of inanimate matter, though the intervals of time involved are naturally greater. Severe frost, scorching heat, the over-

whelming weight of ice and the erosive effect of running water demolish nature's mightiest rock formations just as the weather can destroy the works of man. Mountains crumble —admittedly very slowly but visibly —and the loosened soils are washed down to the plains. These degraded mountains must at some stage have been raised up otherwise they would not now be in the course of destruction.

Let us now consider our Sun which is like an enormous nuclear reactor and converts 4·3 million tons (4·37 million tonnes) of matter into energy every second, radiating this enormous energy into space in the form of heat and light. In time the Sun's energy will be exhausted, so it too must have come into existence in the distant past. The same is true for the legions of stars we see in the night sky, for each star is a distant sun similar to ours and just as transitory. Earth is a planet which means (as will be seen in Chapter 7) that it is a child of the Sun and as such could not have existed before the Sun.

If we study the night sky with large telescopes we find, isolated from each other in the vast expanses of the universe, great agglomerations each of more than 100,000 million stars. These great collections of stars are called galaxies, like our own galaxy the Milky Way, and they are the mightiest cosmic units known, each effectively forming a universe in itself. They too cannot have existed from eternity in the form in which we observe them because, in the course of time, they must exhaust the matter from which new stars are formed and thus decay.

Is this phenomenon, this cycle of birth, existence and death, true of the universe as a whole? Could it not be that it *has* existed from eternity, and what we hold to be its origin is in fact merely a step in a cycle which has transformed the universe from a previous state into its present condition? Are not in fact almost all the natural processes we see around us on Earth cyclical, and is this a universal law? Falling rain becomes spring water, streams and rivers carry it to the sea where it is vaporized by the Sun to form clouds from which the rain falls again. Is it not possible to interpret the cosmic processes of evolution and decay in this way? Stars diffuse their energy by radiation into space and from this dispersed energy new matter is formed. This eventually collects and condenses to form clouds of gas and dust and eventually from these stars once more arise. However, the universe as a whole remains constant, does not decay, and for this reason cannot be said to have come into existence.

This is the theory of "continuous creation" or the steady state theory. The individual steps in the cycle are considered to be quite feasible. However, apart from the fact that such an explanation avoids the central question, namely how the universe came into being, there are other reasons why such a cycle cannot continue indefinitely.

One of these is the second principle of thermodynamics which states that in the long term heat energy can only travel from places of high temperature to places of lower temperature and never the other way round, just as water can only flow downhill. If a body is to emit light or heat by radiation it must be hotter than its surroundings. When it radiates heat, however, it becomes cooler and its surroundings become warmer. This process continues until the temperature difference has been cancelled out. What happens when this stage is reached? No celestial body, that is no sun or star, can radiate energy any longer because it is at the same temperature as its environment. This state is called "death by heat exhaustion", that is the star reaches "thermal death point". It is true there are processes which can create higher temperatures again, but that makes no difference in the long term. Since our universe contains millions and millions of energy-radiating stars it cannot have existed from eternity otherwise it would have died long ago from heat exhaustion.

This argument is not proof against all criticism, but there is another compelling reason why the universe cannot be constantly renewing itself in an eternal cycle. It is known that the matter in stars is not completely diffused by radiation. In fact a considerable part of the star remains which is, however, too small to maintain the high pressures and temperatures necessary for energy generation by nuclear means. In other words they are too small to transform themselves entirely into radiated energy and too small also to remain in the cycle outlined above. These stellar remnants would accumulate in the course of time and eventually there would be nothing left but dead stars.

We shall proceed with the idea that the universe as a whole has at some stage come into existence, or that it "began" at some point in time. We are now faced with the question of how this enormous event could have occurred according to our present knowledge of the nature of the universe and of the laws that operate within it.

It is easier for us to understand things which are familiar to us, or close to us in time and space, so we shall first examine some of the simpler questions which will enable us to familiarize ourselves with some of the particular properties of the universe.

CHAPTER 2

ANCIENT
COSMOGONIES

There has never been a culture, primitive or sophisticated, that did not have an explanation for the origin of the world in which we live. By nature man needs an explanation for everything he sees; it is not necessarily the correct one, but it will be accepted until a more satisfactory or plausible one comes along. In addition, we require some knowledge of our origins if we are to have any sort of realistic view of our future. Every cosmogony (a theory of the origin and development of the universe) is an attempt to establish the origin of our world in such a way that its present condition can be seen as the natural and inevitable consequence of the past. From this picture of the past certain lines of development lead us to a position where we can draw conclusions about the future.

While modern scientific cosmogonies deal with the origin of the universe, that is with the origin of the heavenly bodies and Earth, or possibly only discuss particular aspects of the universe, the interest of the ancient cosmogonies focused more on the origin of man and his religious and social orders.

The role of the waters

A striking role is played in these theories of the origin of the universe by "the waters". This was the primeval element from which the world arose. In the Biblical version of the creation, "the Spirit of God moved upon the face of the waters" before the words, "Let there be light" and, as early as 600 B.C. the Greek philosopher Thales of Miletus taught that all forms of life came from water.

The idea is both obvious and reasonable. The sea, with its ever-changing surface, seems to us elemental, shapeless and formless in contrast to the more permanent enduring landscapes. This sea was the source of life and as we know today it possesses a superabundance of the most varied life forms. On land, too, we only find life where there is water. It is understandable, therefore, that man should consider that there was a primeval ocean from which all things developed.

Another feature of the ancient cosmogonies is the idea that there then developed from the primeval sea a twofold, dual-nature element which separated to form Heaven and Earth, and that this pair between them created, directly or indirectly, everything else. In the Sumerian cosmogony it was the wind which separated Heaven and Earth which were so closely intermingled. This image reappears in the Hebrew Spirit of God, that moved over the face of the waters and created Heaven and Earth. In the ancient languages of the Middle East the

The beginning of the Enuma Elish, the Babylonian Epic of Creation, written on a tablet in cuneiform characters.

same word means both "spirit" and "wind"; they both work invisibly. The most remarkable feature of these images is, however, that they recur—albeit in a new guise—in some of the modern theories about the universe. These present the beginning as a sort of distillation of two basic elements which had originally been dissolved in each other.

First let us examine some of the ancient cosmogonies. They were an important feature of each of the ancient human cultures that developed in the Middle East, in particular Babylonia and Egypt, in India, China and Central America.

Sumerian and Babylonian

The Sumerian cosmogony is the oldest known and originated in the Mesopotamian region several thousand years before Christ. The myth begins with the water Nammu, to whom Heaven and Earth were born as twins. At first these were united but later they were separated by the wind Enlil, who forced himself between Heaven and Earth. Thus the ancient Sumerians considered that a "spiritual" or invisible force was necessary before the material world could unfold and develop. Everything else was then created by a god and goddess, Enki and Nintu, who represented fresh water and fertile earth. The water Enki, bubbling from the depths with the rising and falling of the rivers, impregnated the earth Nintu, who gave birth to verdant plants. Only then was man

In ancient cosmogonies, the waters are the primeval element from which all of creation evolves.

created, in order to serve the gods.

In the subsequent Babylonian culture the first work of poetry in human history was created during the 18th century B.C. This is a version of the creation known by its opening words *Enuma elish* ("When on high") and it is also known as the *Epic of Creation*.

"When as yet no heavenly arch
    hung on high,
And below as yet no thing bore
    earthly name,
Then was only Tiamat, the
    Ocean, the source of all things,
It was Tiamat, the bottomless
    waters, who brought forth
    everything,
When all the waters were
    gathered together as one."

The waters "gathered together as one" were the salt water of the Great Mother Tiamat and the fresh water of the first creator Abzu. The waters bore the seeds of life, from which sprang whole generations of gods. The disorderly doings of this horde angered Tiamat and culminated in a battle of fantastic proportions between her and the gods, in which she deployed all the terrors at her disposal—vipers, dragons, monsters, tempests, hounds and vermin. In spite of all these she was defeated when Marduk (the principal god of the Babylonians, the personification of the Sun) drove a stormwind into her gaping jaws to tear her apart.

Marduk then assumed the role of creator and shaped the world out of the corpse of Tiamat which he divided into two. From the one half he created the heavenly firmament and from the other the terrestrial world. The head of Tiamat was turned into a mountain, her breasts became hills and the Tigris and the Euphrates flowed from her eyes. Marduk posted sentries, with orders "not to let the water out", fixed the year with its twelve months and created the shining moon with its changing phases "to mark the course of the days". Mankind on the other hand, "ordained to serve the gods", was created from the blood of the god Kingu, who had rebelled against the gods and fought against them alongside Tiamat.

The Greek account

Another mythological account of the creation is to be found in the stories from ancient Greece. According to Greek mythology, in the beginning was "Chaos", the name given to the shapeless and unordered void.

The Egyptian goddess Isis, sister and wife of Osiris, and mother of the sun god Horus.

Zeus, grandson of Uranus and Gaia (Heaven and Earth), the highest of the Greek gods.

"Truly, first came Chaos and
    then the Earth,
Broad of back, in eternity a seat
    for all the gods
Who dwell on Olympus' snowy
    peak
And in the darkness of Tartarus,
    in the depths of the Earth,
And at the same time: Eros, the
    most beautiful of the eternal
    gods."

These myths tell that in Tartarus, the mighty subterranean world, Erebos was created (which later housed the realm of the shades, the Underworld ruled by Hades) and the Night. Light was then created by the union of Erebos and dark Night.

Earth, however, created of itself first Uranus, the heavenly firmament, "so that it should envelop her completely"; the high mountains, "the gracious abode of goddesses"; and the Ocean Pontus with its roaring surf. Thus the stage was set for the completion of the creation.

Impregnated by Uranus, Earth gave birth to the race of Titans, among them Oceanus the sea and

Right: Ice and cold are features of the Germanic cosmogonies. Life awakes in the warmth of spring.

her most terrible child, the cunning Chronos, who was an ancestor of the Olympian gods. The Titan Thetis bore Oceanus 3,000 sons, namely the "swirling rivers of the earth", and the same number of "light-footed daughters", amongst them Europa and Asia. Theia bore the Titan Hyperion the mighty Helios (the Sun), the bright Selene (the Moon) and rosy-fingered Eos (the dawn). She in turn gave birth to the winds and the stars. Strangely enough, mankind only appears in these images incidentally and without any explanation of his origin being offered.

The Germanic account

If we now move to northern Europe we find that in Germanic mythology, Chaos is represented by the primeval abyss, called Ginnungagap, which stretched between Niflheim the land of ice in the north, and Muspelheim the land of fire in the south. Nothing existed of the things of the world.

Rivers of ice flowed gradually from north to south and, out of their meeting with the fire, the giant Ymir was formed. From the melting ice a cow Audumla also arose. She lived on salt from the ice she melted with her tongue. From her udder four streams of milk flowed which nourished Ymir. Then a further being was born from the melting ice—Buri.

Ymir and Buri possessed the faculty of procreation. From Ymir the Ice-giants were descended, from Buri, the gods, including Odin or Wodan. Two races were thereby created which were destined to war with each other until the end of the world.

The sons of Buri attacked and killed Ymir, and then the world was formed from the corpse of Ymir as it was in the Babylonian myth from the corpse of Tiamat. The streams of his blood formed the sea, his flesh became the mainland, his bones the mountains, his teeth the rocks of the sea. From his skull the gods built the arch of heaven and placed it on the backs of four dwarfs who supported it. From his brains the clouds were formed. The sparks of fire flying up from Muspelheim, which hitherto had been dispersed into space, then came to rest in the firmament and became the constellations. The gods regulated the paths of the stars and established the alternation of day and night and the changing of the seasons, which in turn determined the growth of the plants.

Out of the bushy eyebrows of Ymir, the gods built the ramparts of their realm, called Midgard (middle-earth) which was also considered to be the dwelling-place of man. Here stood the great ash tree Yggdrasil, at the centre of the world, the branches of which reached into every corner of the universe. It grew to support and protect the whole world. The inhabited areas were surrounded by the sea, which was in turn bounded by the primeval abyss. In this sea there lived a great serpent, so huge that its coils encompassed all the areas known to man. This was

Yggdrasil, the ash tree of Germanic mythology.

the Midgard-serpent. The people themselves, however, were considered in this legend to have been created by the gods from two tree-trunks found on the beach.

It is clear that these mythical cosmogonies do not provide scientific explanations in our sense of the term. They attempt to give answers to very different questions such as: Where does fighting and war originate and what is the source of rebellion and conflict? Where does kingship and royalty come from and the "God-given" social order? What is the nature of mankind and the purpose behind human existence? They attempt to explain questions which may well be more important than the physics of the origin of the world, and they suggest answers that place much greater social obligations on us than do scientific explanations.

The Biblical account

We now turn to the Biblical cosmogony which is of ancient Jewish

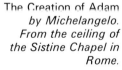

The Creation of Adam by Michelangelo. From the ceiling of the Sistine Chapel in Rome.

origin. In spite of its continued exposition as an explanation for the origin of the world, it is specifically a theological and not a scientific answer. According to the Book of Genesis everything in the universe —light, heaven and earth, stars, land and sea, plants, animals and men—came into being immediately and without exception when God uttered the words, "Let there be...". This explanation is not the description of a physical process but a religious affirmation. To seek in Genesis a scientific explanation of the origin of our universe is a mistake and effectively a disparagement, not least because it is possible to take offence at the inconsistencies in the account—for instance, that day and night were created before the Sun.

The unique character, and thus the primary significance of Genesis lies in the affirmation of a single God-Creator in a world which hitherto had known only innumerable Titans, giants and gods fighting interminably amongst themselves. In this sense the account remains unimpeachable. Towards the end of this book we shall consider the significance of Genesis compared to a scientific cosmogony. The assertions found in Genesis may have been less frequently or widely challenged in earlier times, but we live in an age when everything is questioned and we have become accustomed to seeking rational scientific answers to our questions. We want to know what physical forces and what types of processes created the universe. In the following chapters we shall outline some of these.

The Egyptian pharaoh Ramses I. On his left is Anubis, god of tombs, with the head of a jackal. On his right stands the sun god Horus with falcon's head.

CHAPTER 3

THE STABILITY
OF MATTER

Nothing in the universe can be taken for granted. Many questions which concern us here in terms of Earth are peculiar to our planet and have little significance in relation to the universe. For example, the question of how cold it is in space is pointless because there can be no temperature in a vacuum. The concepts of "above" and "below", which are so natural to us, become confused when we are discussing space, for where there is no gravity there cannot be above or below. All that makes sense is to say that within the solar system there is a favoured direction, that is towards the Sun.

The shape of Earth

Perhaps the question of why Earth is round will provide some surprises. Not only Earth, the Moon and the Sun, but also stars, planets and larger satellites are generally spherical in shape. Since nothing can be taken for granted we must ask why this should be so.

Let us consider that if Earth were completely covered by water it would be perfectly natural for it to be a smooth sphere, for there are no mountains or valleys on the surface of the sea. Every wave collapses at once under its own weight, and we know that water flows downhill until all differences in height have

The ancient Greeks regarded the sphere as the perfect shape.

been cancelled out. That means a spherical shape is achieved. The same is true of the stars, since they are so hot that all the matter of which they are composed is gaseous or at least molten. It follows therefore that they can only be generally spherical in shape. Any major change away from this norm is completely corrected.

But let us consider the Moon, Earth and the other planets in more detail because some at least are solid objects and one might imagine that they could assume any shape.

It is known from experiments that a cube of granite 10^3 cubic centimetres (61 cubic inches) is so solid, that is compact and strong, that it can withstand an applied stress of 1,250,000 newtons (281,000 pounds) without being crushed. If one were

Opposite: *Like most cosmic bodies, Earth is an almost perfect sphere.*

21

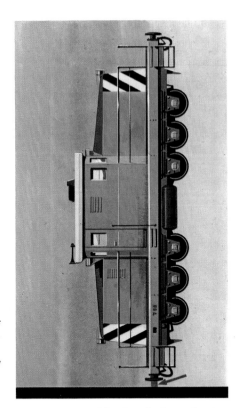

A cube of granite of 1,000 cubic centimetres (61 cubic inches) could support a locomotive weighing 125 tons.

change the shape of Earth from a sphere to a cube. To achieve this one would have to construct, at points corresponding to the eight corners of a cube, eight three-sided pyramids of a height corresponding to the distance from the intersection of the lines drawn tangential to the sphere and the surface of the sphere.

Calculations indicate that these hypothetical pyramids would have to be 4,660,000 metres (15,290,000 feet) high, that is 350 times as high as any pyramid that could possibly be constructed. So the base of the structure would be crushed and destroyed long before we were anywhere near achieving our intention. A structure 13,400 metres (43,965 feet) high (which is the best that one could hope to complete) scaled down to a globe of 32 centimetres (12·6 inches) diameter, would give an elevation of only 0·4 millimetre (0·016 inch). That means that it would not even be visible on a globe at this scale. This is one reason why mountain ranges and ocean depths cannot be represented true to scale on a small model of the planet. At best we could hope to recognize them only by touching them with our finger-tips.

to prepare this load by placing blocks of granite all of this same size one on top of the other, a height of 4,464 metres (14,646 feet) would be reached before the block at the base of the column began to crumble under the combined weight of all the cubes. Each cube weighs 28 newtons (630 pounds) so one would require 1,250,000 divided by 28 = 44,640 cubes before the limit of stress toleration was reached. That would mean a height of 4,464 metres (14,646 feet) or a pillar of granite as high as the Matterhorn. If instead of a straight-sided column one were to build a pyramid, it would reach three times as high because a pyramid constructed on the same base area would weigh only a third as much. That means that theoretically a pyramid could be constructed to a height of 13,400 metres (43,965 feet).

Given the great height of this structure, we could work out if, in theory, it would be possible to

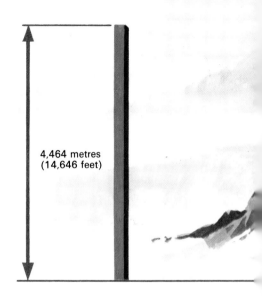

4,464 metres
(14,646 feet)

Our hypothetical calculation shows that a body of the size of Earth can only ever be a sphere—it is immaterial how it came into being, or whether it is gaseous, liquid or solid. That is true for the hardest and most solid of materials we know, of which granite is after all proverbially one. Only very small planetary bodies could have any other shape, because they have small masses and on them our granite pyramids would weigh a negligible amount. This is due to the correspondingly low gravitational force of these bodies.

In the case of bodies of greater dimensions, there are therefore, no "solid" materials in our sense of the word. All materials behave as if they were liquid or at most viscous. Every elevation that exceeds a certain narrow limit, every deviation from the spherical norm, collapses under its own weight and melts like butter in the Sun, until all differences of height are cancelled out. This explains why our planet is spherical in shape, but it is not a perfect sphere as we shall see.

An oblate spheroid

Now we must seek to explain why

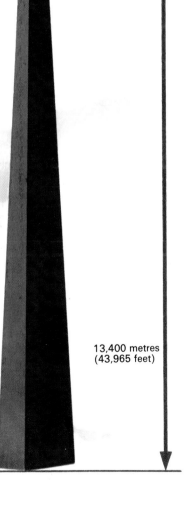

4,478 metres
(14,691 feet)

13,400 metres
(43,965 feet)

We could build a pillar of granite as high as the Matterhorn. Built in the shape of a pyramid, it could be three times as high.

23

Earth is not an *exact* sphere. It is in fact slightly flattened at the north and south poles, just one two hundred and ninety-seventh part ($\frac{1}{297}$) of its diameter, and is referred to as an oblate spheroid. Nevertheless, this flattening is sufficient for Earth's surface to be 21,300 metres (13·2 miles) nearer its centre at the poles than it is at the equator. What causes this difference in height, which is after all almost twice as much as that which we have just calculated to be the greatest possible?

The explanation of this phenomenon lies in the centrifugal force exerted by Earth's speed of rotation which is in excess of 1,609 kilometres (1,000 miles) per hour. This force is negligible at the poles but amounts to 0·034 newton per kilogram (0·0034 pound per pound mass) at the equator. The effect of this force is to cause Earth to swell a little at the equator. So the oblateness of Earth is by no means the remains of a former state which occurred when Earth was liquid and perhaps spun more swiftly on its axis, but rather it is the direct consequence of present circumstances. If Earth were suddenly to stop rotating this oblateness would disappear.

Further, it is of considerable interest that one can draw from the degree of oblateness conclusions concerning the distribution of mass within Earth. The oblateness of a spinning sphere depends upon its distribution of mass as well as upon its rate of spin. If its mass is concentrated mainly in its core, it flattens out to a lesser extent than it would if the mass were regularly distributed or was mainly on the surface (as in the case of a hollow sphere). Earth is less oblate than it would be if its mass were evenly distributed (namely $\frac{1}{297}$ instead of $\frac{1}{230}$). Therefore it must have an exceptionally dense core, believed to be nickel-iron, as can also be established by seismological studies.

Earth's surface

There is a further problem which should be discussed. This concerns the surface relief of the globe. The highest point on Earth is Mount Everest at 8,882 metres (29,002 feet), while the deepest depression in the crust is the Vitiaz Deep in the Marianas Trench at 11,034 metres (36,202 feet) in the western Pacific Ocean. The greatest altitude difference on Earth is therefore 8,882 (29,002) plus 11,034 (36,202) which equals 19,916 metres (65,204 feet) and it is interesting to consider how this is to be reconciled with the greatest possible height, which we calculated to be 13,400 metres (43,965 feet). Admittedly, the cores

To transform Earth from a sphere into a cube, it would be necessary to build on it eight three-sided pyramids each 4·66 million metres (15·29 million feet) high.

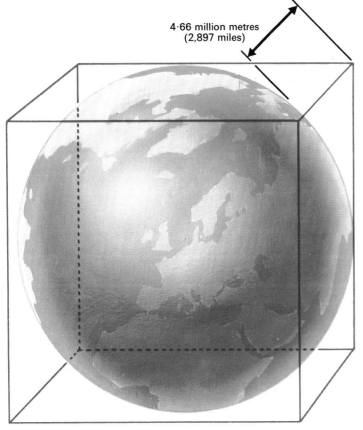

4·66 million metres
(2,897 miles)

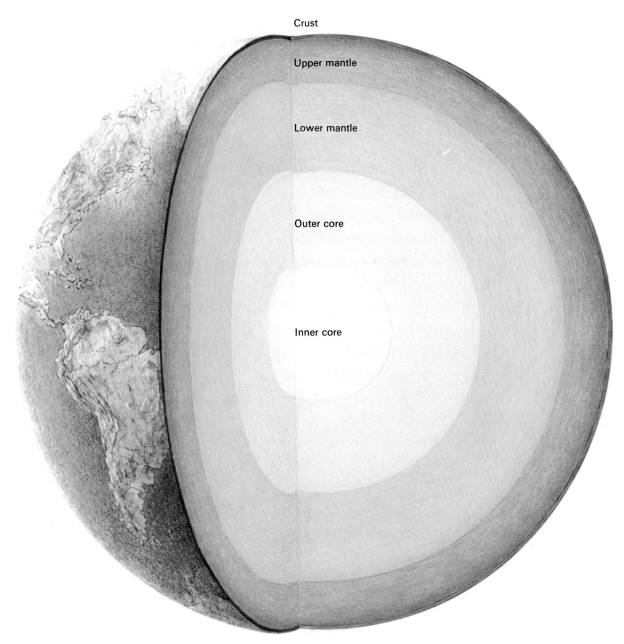

Crust

Upper mantle

Lower mantle

Outer core

Inner core

of the continents are made of granite, the solidity of which has been the subject of our previous calculations. But 11,034 metres (36,202 feet) of the total are immersed in the waters of the ocean and are buoyed up, that is they "float" in the waters of the Pacific. This buoyancy enables them to bear the enormous weight stresses and still remain cohesive.

If we calculate the greatest possible height of a granite pyramid, of which 11,034 metres (36,202 feet) are immersed in water, we arrive at

the figure of 19,873 metres (65,203 feet). That is very close to the actual figure of 19,916 metres (65,204 feet).

In the Marianas Trench, the deepest depression on Earth's surface, stresses are therefore placed on the rocks of the crust which approach the limits of its stress-tolerance. As a result there are constant earth-movements with much rumbling and grinding here. This is a region of great deep sea-quakes and indeed is one of the most earthquake-prone areas on Earth. It can safely be said

Earth's core is of iron and nickel. This heavy core reduces the flattening caused by rotation.

that significantly greater depths will not be found, because they *cannot* exist.

Our earlier discussion has indicated, however, that greater height differences are in fact possible, because they depend on the mass of the body, for instance on the Moon, where everything only weighs one-sixth of what it does on Earth. Unfortunately it is not so easy to

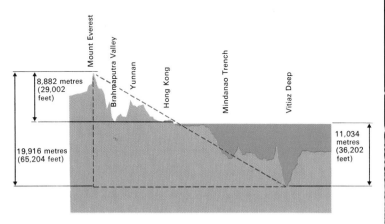

A profile of Earth's surface from the highest point (Mount Everest) to the lowest (the Vitiaz Deep).

It is possible to establish the height of mountains on the Moon from the length of the shadows they cast. In the centre of the picture is the Copernicus crater with walls rising to 4,000 metres (14,450 feet).

ascertain the greatest difference in height on the Moon because of the lack of a unified datum-level or point of reference for altitude measurement such as is provided by the surface of the sea on Earth. The relative heights of mountains can only be established by other methods, such as by comparison with the level of their immediate surroundings. The greatest height measured in this way, employing the length of the shadows cast by the mountain peaks and trigonometrical calculations, amounts to 11,350 metres (37,239 feet), much more than anything on Earth.

So these results of measurements of the relief of the Moon support our calculations and observation. Bodies of these dimensions can only deviate slightly from a basically spherical shape even if they are made of granite, for solidity as we understand the term does not exist.

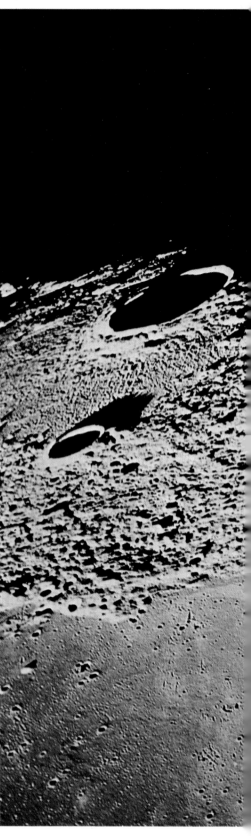

CHAPTER 4

COSMIC
CATASTROPHES

Saturn's ring system

Probably the strangest and most spectacular of the heavenly bodies to observe is Saturn. Like Mars and Jupiter, it is one of our closer neighbours in the solar system. Saturn has ten moons, is just over nine times the size of Earth, almost ten times as far away from the Sun, and is visibly oblate (in the proportion of 1:10). We have seen that this is a sign of fast rotation, in fact it rotates approximately once every ten hours. What gives Saturn its unique position among the planets is its ring system. Even small telescopes are adequate to show that the planet is encircled by a wide, free-floating disc. This is 273,000 kilometres (169,000 miles) in diameter, but amazingly thin—only about 15 kilometres (9·3 miles).

It is quite clear that this is no gigantic, massive, solid ring, for, as we have just seen, solidity in the normal sense which we recognize on Earth does not exist. Even the earliest researchers suspected—and this can be proved by the techniques of modern astronomy—that this ring must be a flat, circular cloud made up of debris, small fragments of matter and cosmic dust, that only looks like a dense ring from a distance.

These early assumptions were based on a law formulated by the

Opposite: *A Moon crater, apparently caused by a body crashing into the surface. Compare Meteor Crater in Arizona shown on page 38.*

The planet Saturn with its system of rings.

The German astronomer Johannes Kepler.

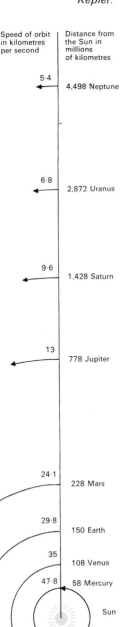

Speed of orbit in kilometres per second	Distance from the Sun in millions of kilometres
5·4	4,498 Neptune
6·8	2,872 Uranus
9·6	1,428 Saturn
13	778 Jupiter
24·1	228 Mars
29·8	150 Earth
35	108 Venus
47·8	58 Mercury
	Sun

German astronomer Johannes Kepler. According to Kepler's Third Law more distant planets revolve round the Sun more slowly than those closer. This also holds true for the rotation of moons round their planets and obviously also for Saturn's ring. The outer edge of the ring is 136,500 kilometres (84,821 miles) from the centre of Saturn; its inner edge, on the other hand, only 75,000 kilometres (46,605 miles). The outer edge accordingly revolves once every 14·6 hours, whereas the inner completes a revolution in only 5·8 hours. Therefore the ring cannot be one solid mass.

How could this ring have been formed? The idea that millions of small bodies could have come together to form such a regular and compact structure by pure chance is one that scientists regard as highly improbable. Some very strict logical process must have determined its formation.

Kepler's Third Law, which correlates distance and orbiting speed is regulated by Newton's Law of Gravity. We understand gravity to mean that force by which all masses attract each other. Newton's Law states that this force of attraction increases with the sizes of the masses involved and their proximity to each other, and that the force is inversely proportional to the square of the distance between them; that means that, when the distance is halved, the force of attraction is quadrupled. What we call "weight" is no more than the gravitational pull of Earth, the force with which it attracts all masses. Thus all weights are lighter on the Moon, because it has a much smaller mass than Earth; in fact they amount to only a sixth of their equivalent on Earth.

The Law of Gravity tells us that a planet will exert less attraction on its moon the farther apart the two bodies are. Since this force of attraction and the centrifugal force generated by the revolution of the moon have to be in a state of balance if the moon is to remain in a constant orbit, then it follows that, in the case of a more distant moon, the centrifugal force must also be smaller. It means that the moon must revolve round its planet more slowly. This, in effect, is precisely what Kepler's Third Law states.

Since a moon is a three-dimensional body, its various parts will be at various distances from its planet, and they would, strictly speaking, have to move at different speeds. The half of the moon facing the planet would have to move faster than the half away from the planet, precisely because it is nearer to it. That sounds like sophistry; but let us see where the idea leads.

The centre of our Moon is 384,405 kilometres (238,869 miles) from Earth. The orbiting speed which Kepler's Third Law stipulates for this distance is 3,683 kilometres (2,288 miles) per hour. This enables the Moon to complete an orbit in just a month. However, this speed is only precise for the centre of the Moon. Those parts of the Moon which face away from, and are thus farthest from Earth, must cover a lot more ground in one orbital revolution because they lie farther out—1,738 kilometres (1,079 miles) (that is the radius of the Moon) farther out. Therefore, they travel faster and that means too fast,—for according to Kepler's Third Law they should travel more slowly.

In these parts of the Moon, the balance between the attraction of Earth and centrifugal force has been disturbed. Centrifugal force predominates, admittedly only by 0·05 millinewton per kilogram (0·005 pound per pound mass), but there has to be some force which holds

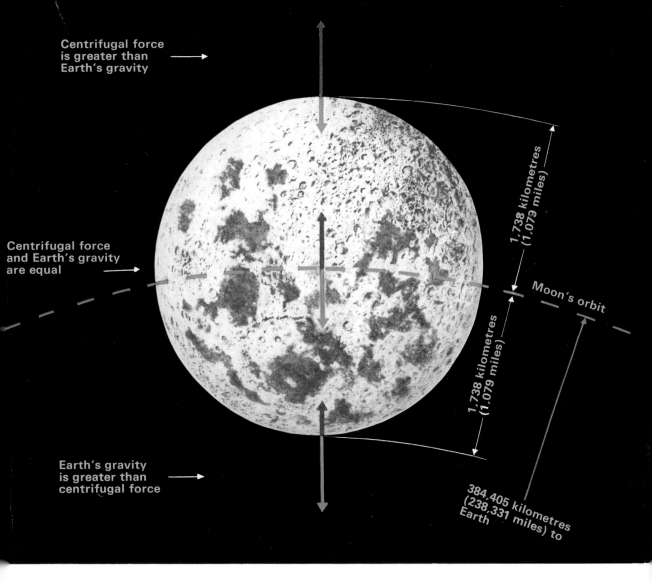

Centrifugal force
is greater than
Earth's gravity →

Centrifugal force
and Earth's gravity
are equal →

Earth's gravity
is greater than
centrifugal force →

1,738 kilometres
(1,079 miles)

Moon's orbit

1,738 kilometres
(1,079 miles)

384,405 kilometres
(238,331 miles) to
Earth

this weight in check just as a cornering car is held on the road by the camber. The restraining force which holds this weight in check on the Moon is the gravity of the Moon, in other words the weight that on the Moon is equal to 1·65 newtons per kilogram (0·168 pound per pound mass).

The opposite is true of those parts of the Moon which face Earth and are thus nearest to it. Here the attraction of Earth predominates, and since this force is directed away from the Moon, a weight-loss is also to be found here.

We could maintain that 0·05 millinewton is insignificant, but even this amount has an effect, since the Moon as a planetary body has no solidity in the ordinary sense of the word. The Moon is in fact stretched a little, away from Earth where centrifugal force predominates, and towards Earth where Earth's attractions predominates. These opposing forces tend to distort it into a slight egg-shape, not by much, merely a few kilometres, but this deformation can be established by very precise measurements.

The consequences of this distortion would be more significant, however, if our Moon were orbiting nearer to Earth. If the Moon were 100,000 kilometres (62,000 miles)

In those parts of the Moon facing away from Earth, centrifugal force is greater than Earth's gravitational pull. In those parts facing Earth the opposite is true.

According to Kepler's Third Law, planets orbit the Sun more slowly the farther they are from it.

31

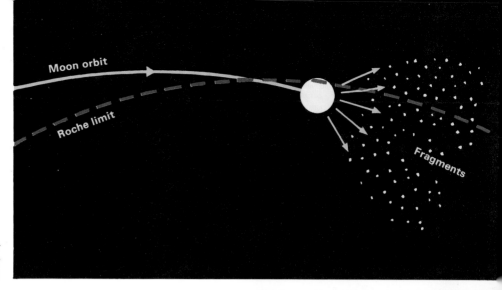

A moon is torn apart if it crosses its planet's Roche limit.

away, the weight-loss from those parts of it nearest to, and farthest from, Earth would amount to 2·07 millinewtons (0·00046 pound). At 20,000 kilometres (12,400 miles) the weight-loss would be 0·26 newton (0·058 pound) and at 10,400 kilometres (5,960 miles) it would reach 1·65 newtons (0·37 pound). That is the actual weight of a kilogram on the Moon, and is the force by which the Moon holds its constituent parts together.

So there exists for every satellite a distance or interval from its primary planet at which weight-loss suddenly becomes equal to the weight of the body itself—this has been called the Roche limit after the French mathematician who first discovered it. Any moon or other planetary body that exceeds this limit suffers a catastrophic fate. During its close approach to the limit the satellite becomes elongated, and those parts which are nearest to, and farthest from, the planet break off from it. The latter are carried out by the dominant centrifugal force until their decreasing speed corresponds to the distance they have reached from the centre (following Kepler's Third Law). The former are pulled correspondingly closer towards the primary planet.

Since the gravity of the moon is

This exaggerated illustration shows how the Moon is distorted into an egg-shape by centrifugal force on the one hand and Earth's attraction on the other.

Centrifugal force dominant

Moon orbit

Earth's gravity dominant

North Pole

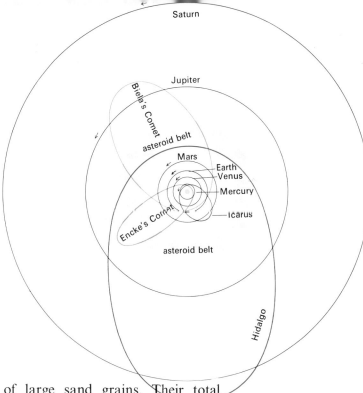

steadily reduced by this loss of mass, it now becomes totally impossible for it to hold together and it disintegrates completely. Nothing but debris is left, the fragments of which are comparatively small measured in cosmic terms. These small fragments of low mass are the only ones whose "solidity" can hold them together.

The debris produced by the disintegration of the satellite is spread over a wide area and forms a broad, flat ring, the distribution of which is determined by the varying orbiting speeds of the individual fragments round the primary planet. If we now turn to Saturn, we find its ring lies within the planet's Roche limit. This suggests certain conclusions concerning the origin of the ring, namely that one of Saturn's moons, or some other satellite body, passed or orbited too close to the planet. During its close approach it was destroyed and formed the ring of debris that gives Saturn its unique appearance today. Another possibility for the origin of the ring system will be discussed in Chapter 7.

We shall now consider the position of our Moon and its relationship to Earth. The Roche limit of Earth lies about 10,400 kilometres (5,960 miles) from the centre of the planet. The Moon is 384,405 kilometres (238,869 miles) away so there is not much likelihood of Earth developing a ring like Saturn's.

The asteroid belt

The process which gave Saturn its ring is also generally accepted as the origin of the asteroid belt. These minor planets are small bodies which orbit the Sun in a broad band between the planets Mars and Jupiter. They vary in size from the largest, Ceres (780 kilometres (485 miles) in diameter) down to the size

of large sand grains. Their total number is unknown, but our best telescopes enable us to estimate their number at about 44,000. In some cases, variations in light-intensity lead us to assume that they are irregularly shaped bodies.

Between the planets Mars and Jupiter, a large swarm of asteroids orbit the Sun in place of a "missing" planet.

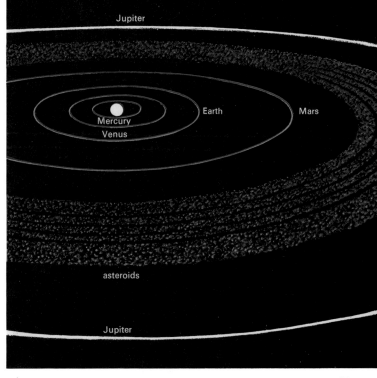

What makes them especially interesting is the fact that they orbit the Sun at a position in the solar system where a planet proper is "missing". The intervals at which planets revolve round the Sun conform to an empirical law known as Bode's Law. Apart from one simple exception, this law can be summed up by stating that, using Mercury as the starting-point, each planet in the solar system is twice as far from the Sun as the previous planet. According to Bode's Law there should be a planet between Mars and Jupiter, but instead we find a broad belt of asteroids, which appear to be the remains of a planet which had earlier occupied this orbit.

We shall see, when we discuss the origin of the solar system, that they could also consist of matter or debris from the cloud which surrounded the Sun in its youthful stage of development but which never condensed to form a planet. But there is a lot of evidence to suggest that they are fragments of quite a large planet. How then could they have been formed?

There are some people determined to believe that this "planet" was inhabited by beings as unreasonable as humans and that it was destroyed by a nuclear war or some catastrophe of that nature. But there is a much more plausible explanation. When two planets come very close to each other in their orbits round the Sun—a position we call "conjunction"—they exert a very strong attraction on each other in accordance with the Law of Gravity. This is the phenomenon that led to the discovery of the planet Neptune.

An unknown planet

The path of the planet Uranus had been constantly revealing inexplicable disturbances or perturbations. The cause was assumed to be an unknown planet the gravitational pull of which was deflecting Uranus from its path. From these disturbances in the orbital path, the French mathematician Leverrier undertook to calculate the position of this unknown planet. It was a triumph for mathematical astronomy when it was in fact found in the expected place.

Every planet will pull or deflect its neighbour from its orbit in this way in the event of a "conjunction". When the orbiting times of the planets are not in a simple numerical relationship, this occurs at various, changing points along the orbit and so balances itself out over long periods of time.

If, on the other hand, in the time

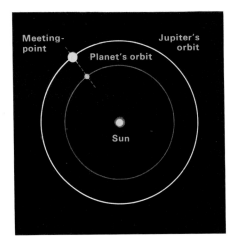

When neighbouring planets approach each other at the closest point in their orbits, the larger planet exerts attraction on the smaller.

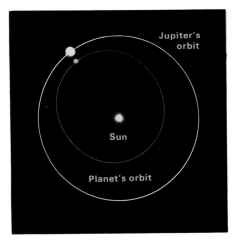

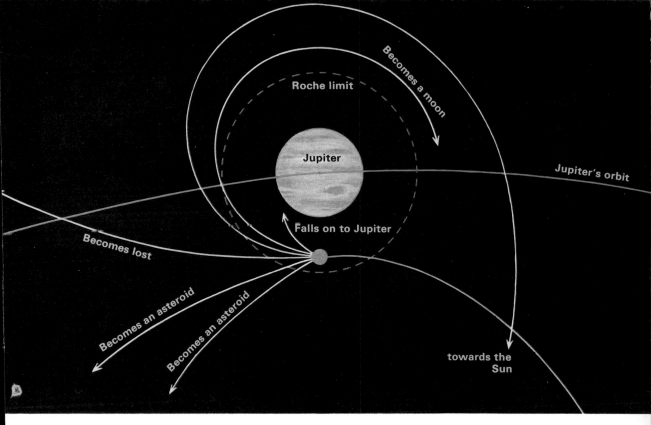

Labels on figure:
- Becomes a moon
- Roche limit
- Jupiter
- Jupiter's orbit
- Becomes lost
- Falls on to Jupiter
- Becomes an asteroid
- Becomes an asteroid
- towards the Sun

that a planet takes to complete its orbit, its inner neighbour can complete two (if, that is, their orbiting times are in the simple numerical relationship of 1 : 2), then the planets will continually meet at the same point. Then the dislocating effects are cumulative and in time the paths of the two planets converge more and more at this meeting-point. They finally get so close that a cosmic catastrophe becomes inevitable.

It is, therefore, decisive for the continuance of our solar system that the numerical relationships of the planetary orbiting times are not simple; they are 31 : 12, 47 : 35, 35 : 14, and so on. Thus our solar system is stable.

The missing planet between the orbits of Mars and Jupiter *was* threatened, however. Its orbiting-time, according to Bode's Law, could have stood in a relationship of 2 : 5 to that of Jupiter. That means Jupiter would not have been in place on every second orbit of the ill-fated planet, only on every fifth orbit.

However, Jupiter has by far the greatest mass of all the planets (more than twice as great as all the others put together!), and so the greatest force of attraction. As a result these conjunctions, which under other circumstances would perhaps not have been critical, became very dangerous for its neighbour.

In accordance with the mechanical laws of the universe the orbital path of the planet, which like all others had originally been almost circular and concentric within that of Jupiter, now started to become elongated in the direction of this meeting-point (which fell always in the same place). There was no need for a direct collision with Jupiter; it was quite sufficient for the ill-fated planet to cross Jupiter's Roche limit for it to suffer the same fate as the shattered Saturn moon. What do we know of this planet and of the fate of its remains?

It cannot have been very large, otherwise it would, in its turn, have altered Jupiter's orbital path, but no

If a small body crosses the Roche limit of a larger body it is destroyed. This was probably the fate of a smaller body which came too close to Jupiter.

Left: *No asteroids pass along paths with orbiting times in a simple numerical relationship to Jupiter's. These gaps in the swarm are called "Kirkwood gaps".*

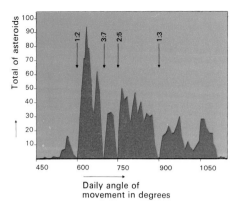

Right: *Kirkwood gaps are also found in Saturn's ring system, where orbiting times stand in a simple numerical relationship to that of one of Saturn's moons.*

Over large areas the surface of the Moon is scarred by the impact of meteorites. It is possible that these are traces of asteroids which crashed into the Moon.

traces of any such disturbance can be found. The total mass of all the asteroids has been calculated at approximately one-thousandth of Earth's mass. If one assumes from the size-distribution of the other planets that originally this planet was approximately the size of Earth, then the bulk of its mass must have been lost in the catastrophe. The remaining thousandth is orbiting, shattered into thousands of fragments and dispersed far and wide, in the area between Mars and Jupiter where the path of the planet had lain. It constitutes the cosmic bodies which we call asteroids.

We can see without further explanation that no asteroid can maintain itself for long if its orbiting time is in a simple numerical relationship to that of Jupiter. It would meet the same fate as the doomed planet. We find Kirkwood gaps (named after Daniel Kirkwood an American astronomer who discovered the relationships) with the numerical relationships 1:2, 1:3, 2:5 and 3:7. In these areas we find no, or at best, very isolated asteroids.

We also find Kirkwood gaps in Saturn's ring system. Everywhere that we find orbiting-times in simple numerical correspondence to the orbiting time of one of Saturn's moons, we find a dark "gradation" of the ring, an area in which no debris revolves. No fragment could remain there because it would be drawn out by the force of attraction of a moon. The ring is, therefore, a "system of rings", a structure of several concentric discs.

As far as the remaining material of the shattered planet is concerned, we must assume that the fragments were so completely swept from their path by the overpowering gravity of near-by Jupiter that they were thoroughly dispersed in all directions. Part of this debris was lost in space; part rained down on to Jupiter, and some fragments were probably captured as moons by Jupiter and Saturn. The main part, however, probably fell into the Sun (which is, after all, the direction

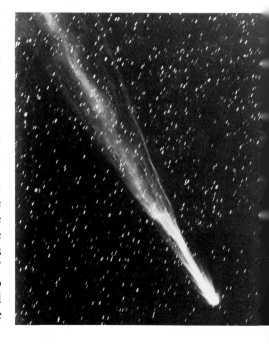

"downwards" in the solar system). A mighty hail of planet debris must have fallen on the inner planets— Mars, Earth, Venus and Mercury. Perhaps the scarring of the surface, which we can observe on the Moon and on Mars and will very probably find on Mercury, too, can be traced back to the impact of such fragments. On Earth, any traces of this distant catastrophe have been eliminated by the process of erosion. The same may be true of Venus, for it too has a dense atmosphere.

Comets, meteors and meteorites

Small and minute fragments of this ill-fated planet could partly explain the origins of comets, meteors and meteorites. Comets used to be seen as ill-omens, like everything that did not seem to fit into the universal order. Indeed they mostly appear unexpectedly and on unusual paths, and with their long tails they must have had a somewhat unnerving effect on people who did not know what they were. Many superstitious ideas surround them.

Comets travel along paths that, in contrast to the planets, are very elongated ellipses, that take them far from the Sun out into space, and then bring them back into close proximity with the Sun. They are probably sizeable accumulations of several thousand tons of solid particles with elements of carbon, hydrogen, oxygen, carbon monoxide and nitrogen. When they approach the Sun, the gases which had hitherto been frozen, become vaporized. Part of the light is scattered sunlight, the remainder is that triggered off by the Sun's radiation, a fluorescence much like the neon in our gas-discharge lamps. When the gases become ionized they form the visible head and tail of the comet.

Asteroids occasionally have similar elliptical paths, but they are not quite so eccentric. One called Hidalgo wanders out as far as Saturn and back almost as far as Mars. Another, called Icarus, even penetrates the path of Mercury. At one point it comes sufficiently close to Earth to be detectable by radar. It is possible, therefore, that there is some relationship between comets and some asteroids. On the other hand, there are comets that appear to come to us from such distances in space, that it seems unlikely they originate within our solar system. The origin of comets is still not clearly established.

Meteors and shooting stars are mostly very small bodies which cause light-effects when they burn up as they penetrate our atmosphere. If they are very small grains they become shooting stars, which burn out at a height of about 100 kilometres (62 miles) above Earth's surface. If they are larger, they become meteors or fire-balls which penetrate farther into the atmosphere and occasionally reach Earth's surface, where under favourable conditions they can sometimes be found. These bodies are known as meteorites. Before the American and Russian space programmes collected Moon rocks, they were the only examples of extra-terrestrial matter available to us, and therefore, of the greatest interest. Many are about the size of a fist, and they consist partly of silicate rocks and partly of metallic minerals—such materials of which Earth is composed. Since these minerals can only be formed under high temperature and pressure, such as are found in the deep interior of a planet, they support the assumption that these fragments are the remains of a shattered planet.

The biggest meteorites, with weights estimated at several million tons, create on impact with Earth

As comets used to be regarded as ill-omens, they were depicted as frightening objects.

Left: *The Morehouse Comet in 1908. The tail is formed of gases separated from the main body of the comet.*

37

enormous meteorite craters. Examples of some of the largest include Meteor Crater in Arizona, one in the north-west of Quebec Province, Canada and the Nördlinger Ries in southern Germany.

There are always exceptionally impressive and numerous falls of meteors and shooting stars when Earth passes through the path, or more particularly the tail, of a comet. It is very likely, therefore, that comets are closely related to meteors and meteorites.

In conclusion, it is also very likely that the asteroids, comets and meteors are all members of the same family, and are probably the remains of a planet which once orbited between Jupiter and Mars and which was destroyed by the same sort of forces which gave Saturn its ring system.

This force of gravity which holds the planets in their orbits round the Sun and which keeps the Moon in its orbit round Earth, acts between all objects however large or small. In normal, everyday life on Earth, the most obvious effect of gravity is that any unsupported object will fall to the ground. The acceleration of such an object towards Earth has been found to have a constant value regardless of its weight. This means that a heavy and a light object released from the same height will strike the ground at the same time.

Opposite: *The famous Meteor Crater or Crater Mound in central Arizona (U.S.A.). It is 174 metres (600 feet) deep and 1,280 metres (4,000 feet) across, and was formed tens of thousands of years ago.*

The Nördlinger Ries in Bavaria is a meteorite crater 25 kilometres (15·6 miles) in diameter. It was formed between fifteen and twenty million years ago.

CHAPTER 5

HOW DID
EARTH ACQUIRE
ITS MOON?

The question of why our Moon is where it is occupied men's minds long before there was any possibility of landing there. Various possibilities have been discussed for a very long time, so we can examine them and test their feasibility.

The striking thing about the Moon is its disproportionate size compared with other satellite bodies of its kind. It has a diameter of 3,476 kilometres (2,158 miles), more than a quarter of Earth's. It is the fifth biggest moon in the solar system, whereas the largest moon of all, Jupiter's Ganymede, reaches only one-thirtieth of Jupiter's diameter. Furthermore, the Moon's orbital path is unusually far from Earth in comparison with other similar satellites; it is at a distance of sixty-one times the radius of Earth, whereas the outermost major moon of Jupiter is only at a distance from the planet of twenty-six times the radius of Jupiter.

How could our Moon have originated? We must begin by examining some of the physical mechanics of the universe.

According to Kepler's First Law, heavenly bodies always revolve round each other in "conic sections" that is ellipses, parabolae or hyperbolae, in which the heavier body effectively provides the focus. The ellipses can be almost circular, as in the case of the planets, or very elongated as with the comets, and when a body approaches us from the infinite reaches of space, its ellipse becomes parabolic or hyperbolic.

A fragment of Earth

The view has been put forward that at some time in the distant past another celestial body, for example a huge meteorite or perhaps even a fragment of the doomed planet we discussed in Chapter 4, collided with Earth and blasted a huge piece out of it. Calculations show that meteorites of more than one hundred tons

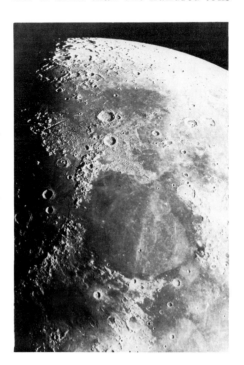

Opposite: *A part of the side of the Moon which never faces Earth.*

Northern area of the Moon with the Caucasus.

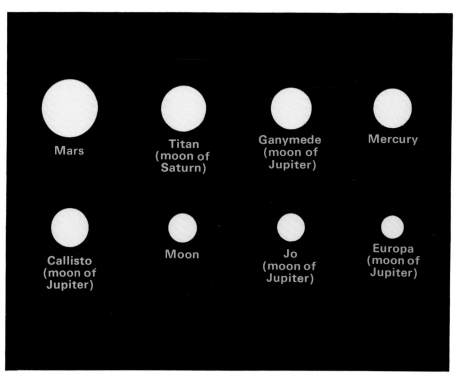

Mars

Titan
(moon of
Saturn)

Ganymede
(moon of
Jupiter)

Mercury

Callisto
(moon of
Jupiter)

Moon

Jo
(moon of
Jupiter)

Europa
(moon of
Jupiter)

Moon

Callisto

Ganymede

Europa

Jo

Earth

are completely vaporized by the kinetic energy released on impact— that means that they act like an explosive charge. It has been suggested that the fragment broken off by this explosion is the Moon and the hole created is the great basin of the Pacific Ocean.

This view is based on the firmly held belief that matter is sufficiently stable for this to happen. However, we know that a fragment the size of the Moon would not hold together on release, as would a small piece of shrapnel, but would be completely shattered, because it is not "solid" in the normal sense. The great Pacific basin does not need an explanation of this sort either. It was created by purely geological factors. The substratum which underlies the ocean basins is made of denser rock than the continents which tend to "float" on this heavier substratum.

Above all, this assumed process of satellite formation is totally irreconcilable with the most basic laws

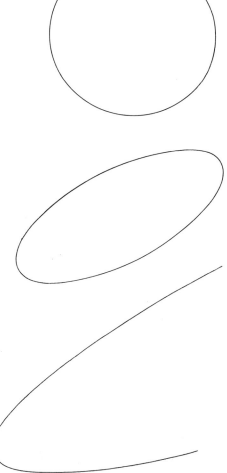

Moon's path

Path of an
ejected body

A body ejected from
Earth would return to
Earth along an
elliptical path. It
would never go into
orbit round Earth.
This is why it is
necessary constantly
to adjust the course
of a rocket for some
time after lift-off.

of astrophysics. If such a fragment were hurled out into space, it would either describe an ellipse in accordance with Kepler's First Law (and since an ellipse is defined as a closed curve, the fragment would inevitably return to its starting-point, Earth, after one revolution), or, if propelled with sufficient velocity, would be sent completely out of Earth's gravitational pull and be lost for ever. A fragment which is fired from Earth, however high into space it moves, will fall back to Earth like a stone tossed in the air (unless it is completely lost in the depths of space) and will certainly never achieve an almost circular orbit round Earth like that of the Moon. This is why rockets have to be directed to change course after lift-off, so that they go into orbit instead of falling back to Earth. So our Moon cannot have originated in this way, for we have to explain not only its presence but also the shape of its orbit.

Earth

Foreign body

Another theory

A second theory avoids this difficulty. This is based on the assumption that Earth used to rotate more quickly than it does now. If our day had been about four instead of twenty-four hours long, Earth would have been extremely oblate and would have had a diameter at the equator 2·5 times as great as it has. Under these circumstances, centrifugal force would have been strong enough to cancel out gravitational pull at the equator. Then one part of Earth would have become separated

from the main bulk to form the Moon which would then have been seized by "tidal forces" to carry it away from Earth, at first quickly, but subsequently at ever decreasing speeds. The theory maintains that this process is not complete and that consequently the Moon is even today drifting away from Earth at the rate of 12·5 centimetres (4·9 inches) a year.

The creation of the Moon in this way would, like the raising of a lever, consume energy. This energy is as-

Far left: *Compared
with other moons in
the solar system, and
the distances
between them and
their planets, our
Moon is exceptionally
big and far away
from its planet, Earth*

Opposite above: *The
relative proportions of
some large moons
and small planets.*

Opposite right: *A
planetary orbit
(almost circular), a
comet's path
(elongated ellipse)
and a parabola (open
curve).*

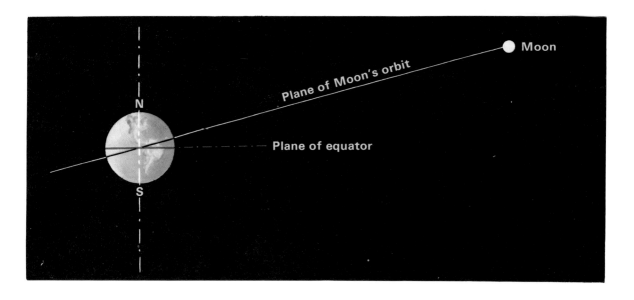

The plane of the Moon's orbital path lies at an angle of 28.7 degrees to Earth's equator.

sumed to have come from the rotation of Earth, which is to be considered as a gigantic fly-wheel, so that Earth's rotation slowed down and the day was extended to its present length. It has been calculated that in the last 120,000 years the day has become longer by one second.

Theoretically, the "tidal forces" mentioned above could, in fact, exist but they are so extraordinarily minute that nobody has yet succeeded in establishing their real size. They are concerned with complex interactions between the Moon and the tides it creates on Earth, but further consideration of them here would make little sense, as there are several reasons why the Moon cannot have originated in this way.

If one calculates the rotational energy of Earth in a revolution lasting four hours, and one lasting twenty-four hours, the difference is not sufficient to cause the Moon to move to such a distance from Earth.

According to this hypothesis, the Moon was broken off by centrifugal force at the equator. So it should still today be orbiting above the equator. This is not the case. Its orbital path lies almost exactly on the plane of

the planetary orbital paths, which is at an angle of 23 degrees to the plane of the equator.

The irrefutable objection however is that, according to this theory, the Moon originated within Earth's Roche limit. Since no satellite can survive within this region, it is totally inconceivable that any could have originated there. So this theory appears to be groundless too.

A third theory

A third view is that the Moon is a body which was captured by the gravitational attraction of Earth, when its orbit passed close to that of our planet. However, Kepler's First Law, which deals precisely with the effects of this force of attraction, states that such a body describes a parabola or hyperbola. Both of these are open curves which, even after tangential contact with Earth, would still lead the floating body back off into space, never to return. So it would appear that the Moon has not been captured.

Nevertheless we cannot be satisfied with this answer without further investigation; for there are moons which *have* almost certainly been

Opposite: *The seven outer moons of Jupiter form an irregular group — in contrast to the planet's five orderly inner moons.*

captured by other planets, namely the seven outer moons of Jupiter and the outermost moon of Saturn. So this is not an exceptional phenomenon.

The five inner moons of Jupiter and the eight inner moons of Saturn orbit in planes very close to that of their planet's equators. They also orbit in almost concentric circles and in the same direction as the planets themselves revolve. They are obviously strictly related to the planets, they must have originated in the closest association with them, and so they must always have belonged to them. The seven outer moons of Jupiter and Saturn's most distant moon, on the other hand, are not only separated from the others by a conspicuous gap, and are much smaller than them (typically about one-hundredth of the diameter of the inner moons), but they have very elliptical orbits. Some of them even travel "backwards", in other words in the opposite direction to that in which the planet itself is revolving. They are apparently incidental to the planet and are, therefore, probably captured.

It follows from this that it must be possible for a planet to capture a moon, and this is most likely to happen: if the planet is very large, like Jupiter or Saturn, and thus has strong gravitational pull; if the captured body is of modest size, like the eight named above; if the body approaches the planet along a path which conforms to the planet's path; and if it is moving at a speed only slightly in excess of the planet's speed.

All these conditions cannot be fulfilled by bodies originating outside the solar system. Every body that comes from deep space travels on parabolic or hyperbolic paths, the shape of which is too far removed from that of a planetary path, and at too high speeds. So the eight unusual moons of Jupiter and Saturn are probably captured asteroids, since those are the only bodies capable of fulfilling the conditions of size, shape of orbital path and speed.

It is considered impossible, however, that Earth could have captured an asteroid as a moon in this way. Firstly, Earth is much too small. Its mass amounts to only one-hundredth of that of Saturn, and only one three-hundredth of the mass of Jupiter. Also the Moon is much too large and therefore heavy. Its mass is more than a thousand times as great as the mass of the largest asteroid captured by Jupiter or Saturn. Finally, its path could, it is true, have adapted to a certain extent to the path of Earth (as we saw in Chapter 4), but then its speed would have been much too great. An asteroid whose path carried it close to Earth, would have a speed of 50 kilometres (31 miles) per second as opposed to Earth's 30 kilometres (18·5 miles) per second. If Earth could have influenced the asteroid during this short period of proximity in such a way that its path became the orbital path of a satellite-moon, then this path would be extremely eccentric like those of the eight captured moons, and not almost circular like that of our Moon. So it is reasonable to assume that our Moon was not captured.

What makes our Moon such a special case is the fact that, of all the moons in the solar system, it is the only one that orbits *outside* the sphere in which its planet's gravitational pull exceeds that of the Sun.

If we were to place an object between Earth and the Sun, it would normally fall into the Sun because its gravitational pull is much stronger than that of Earth. Only if it were nearer than 262,000 kilometres (162,000 miles) to Earth would the

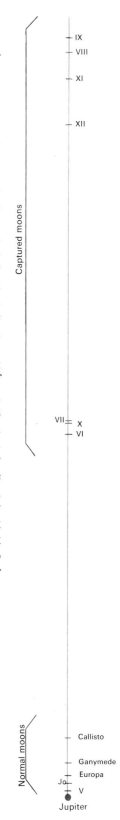

If the orbit of an asteroid is affected by the gravitational pull of a major planet, the asteroid can be captured and become a moon.

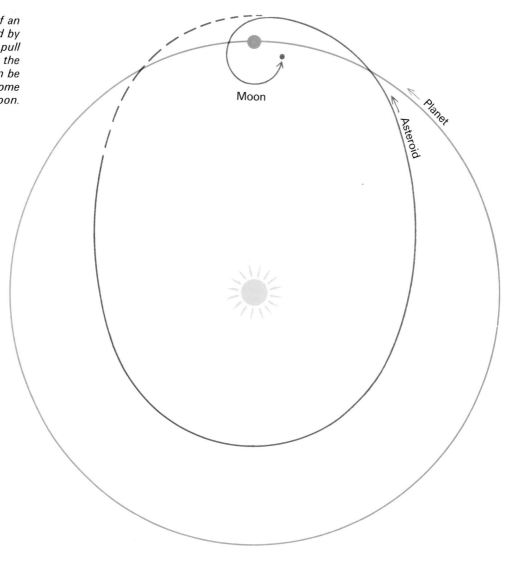

Moon

Planet

Asteroid

Moon's orbit

Earth's orbit

Path of Jupiter's moon

Jupiter's orbit

object fall to Earth, because beyond this point, the Sun's gravity dominates. Yet our Moon orbits outside this limit, at 384,000 kilometres (238,000 miles). We could, therefore, justifiably say that it belongs to the Sun rather than Earth. Its path is determined primarily by the Sun and only incidentally by Earth.

If we draw the Moon's orbital path correctly to scale, as the illustration shows, it is clear that one cannot say that the Moon revolves round Earth and is thus controlled by Earth in its path round the Sun, as is the case with Jupiter and its moons. The Moon revolves round the Sun and is swung round the sky a little by Earth—so little in fact, that it would make hardly any noticeable difference to its path if Earth were taken away. In other words, the Moon travels in reality on a planetary track which is slightly "disturbed" by Earth.

Moreover, it is practically the size of a planet and orbits almost in the plane of the planetary paths. From these facts it can be said that it is not a moon so much as a rather small planet. Earth and the Moon constitute a double planet, or twin planets that orbit the Sun on the same track and revolve round each other in the process. So Earth cannot be said to have captured its moon at some time subsequent to its own creation; it has always had it. They came into being simultaneously as planets. How this event is believed to have occurred is discussed in Chapter 7.

Although the Moon can almost be thought of as a small planet, the conditions on its surface are vastly different from those on its nearest neighbour, Earth. It is known that the Moon does not have an appreciable atmosphere, and also that the surface temperature varies from about −100 °C (−146 °F) during the lunar night to more than 100 °C (212 °F) during the lunar day. The lack of a lunar atmosphere can be explained by considering the Moon's escape velocity.

The escape velocity of the Moon is 2·4 kilometres (1·5 miles) per second, while that of Earth is 11·2 kilometres (7 miles) per second. Let us suppose that the Moon originally had an atmosphere. With a surface temperature of 100 °C (212 °F), the gas molecules could easily exceed the Moon's escape velocity, but not that of Earth. So any lunar atmosphere would have been lost long ago.

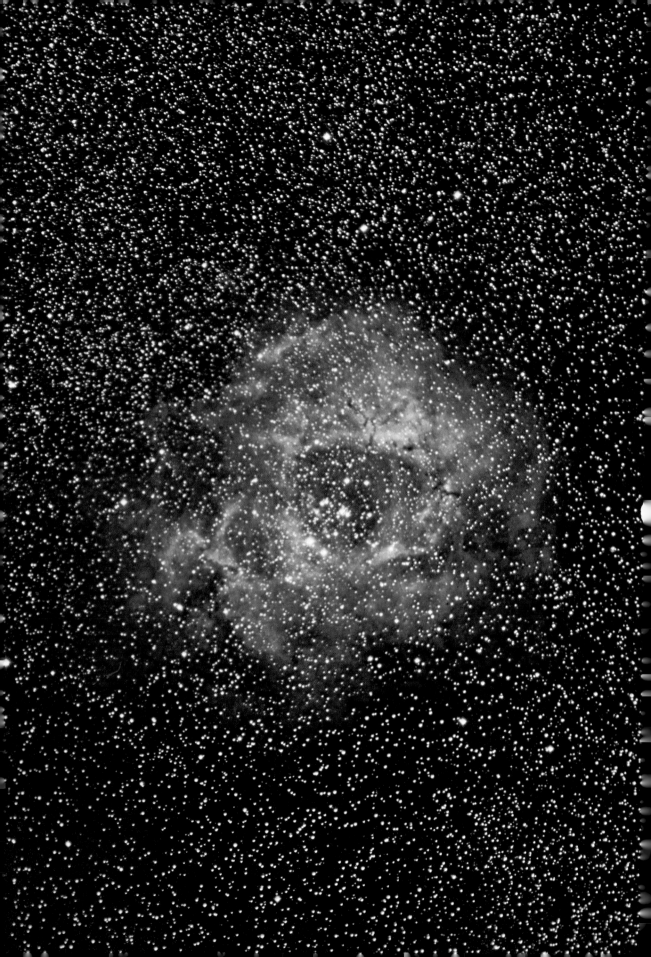

CHAPTER 6

THE ORIGIN
OF THE SUN

A mighty phenomenon

Many people take the Sun for granted just because it is there. But we must admit that it is an incredible phenomenon, a vast storehouse of almost inconceivable power.

There it is at a point in space 148,736,000 kilometres (92 million miles) away from us moving along its path in the galaxy at a speed of 216 kilometres (134 miles) per second. It is an enormous concentration of 2×10^{27} tons of matter comprising primarily the elements hydrogen and helium, but also containing 20×10^{24} tons of other heavier elements. The sphere of the Sun is 1,382,400 kilometres (860,000 miles) in diameter and has a surface temperature which ranges from 4,000 degrees Centigrade (7,232 degrees Fahrenheit) to 5,700 °C (10,292 °F). It has been dispersing $370,000 \times 10^{18}$ kilowatts of energy into space for many thousands of millions of years.

In the distant future the Sun will be exhausted by this mighty generation and dispersion of its energy. The Sun is not constant but like all other stars is at a stage in its evolution, and must continually change and eventually come to an end. At some point in time therefore it must have had a beginning.

It would be very difficult to say anything significant or meaningful about the origin and continuing development of the Sun if it were something unique in the universe. As long as it has been observed and studied by man it has never shown any permanent change. It evolves so slowly that the period of time during which man has observed the Sun in detail is much too short for us to be able to witness significant changes. It is only over periods of thousands of millions of years that important changes would be discernible. However, all stars are suns like ours. The only feature that distinguishes our Sun from all the other stars is its distance from Earth. The nearest star is more than 40,000 times farther from Earth than the Sun is. That is why all the stars appear as delicate points of light, in spite of the fact that many are much larger and brighter than the Sun.

Space between stars

If we look carefully at the night sky it is clear that there are innumerable stars in space, and these are separated from one another by enormous distances. If we can imagine the Sun reduced in scale to the size of a cherry, then the average distance between the stars would be about 1,000 kilometres (620 miles). That would mean the cherries would be distributed with one in London, one in Berlin and one in Moscow, and this is the sort of density with

The Rosette nebula in Monoceros. The Sun originated in a galactic nebula like this.

which these stars occur in space.

Appearances are, however, deceptive and the space between the stars is not completely empty. In fact finely disseminated matter is present together with hydrogen gas at a very low density. Because of this interstellar matter the light of the most distant stars reaching us is a little weaker than it would otherwise be if space were absolutely empty, depending of course on the distance it had to travel. The light is a little redder, just as the setting Sun appears weaker and redder because its light has to pass through more of our atmosphere, the rays coming to us obliquely.

Particles of matter are so widely distributed in space that on average only one atom per 2 cubic centimetres (0·122 cubic inch) occurs as compared with 27×10^{18} molecules per cubic centimetre (442×10^{18} molecules per cubic inch) in our atmosphere. The pressure in the greatest vacuum that we can, with our technical resources, produce on Earth is many millions of times greater than that in the vacuum of space. Spectroscopic and other observations made of space suggest that the interstellar matter consists of 99 per cent gaseous hydrogen, (together with small amounts of helium) and 1 per cent of heavier elements in the form of fine dust particles. These particles measure about one ten-thousandth of a millimetre (one four-millionth of an inch) and are so sparsely distributed that the ratio is only one to 5 million cubic metres (175 million cubic feet).

In spite of this extreme rarefaction, it has been calculated that the total sum of all the matter in the universe is distributed in approximately equal proportions between that concentrated in the stars and the interstellar matter. If this is the case, large if thinly distributed amounts of hydrogen, helium and relatively small quantities of heavier elements in the form of dust exist in space. Young stars are composed of these three groups of particles. So interstellar matter is probably the material from which new stars are formed.

Interstellar matter

Our observations of the night sky indicate that interstellar matter is not evenly distributed in space. Rather it forms irregular accumulations or belts where the concentration is greater than normal, with perhaps two or three atoms per cubic centimetre (30–40 atoms per cubic inch). These rather denser accumulations are present in space and form irregularly moving currents. When they meet and combine they occasionally form areas of greater density. In these areas gravitational forces tend to attract the particles involved in the concentration and strengthen it or increase its density. However, these concentrations of matter separate and become diffused again by the currents which brought them together and by the internal pressures created within such accumulations.

The famous English mathematician and astronomer Sir James Jeans calculated the conditions necessary for the survival of such a concentration of matter. Basically a volume of matter at least one thousand times the mass of the Sun, and with a density of at least 100 atoms per cubic centimetre (1,600 atoms per cubic inch), is required. Only then is the gravitational force within the concentration powerful enough to outweigh the disruptive forces which seek to disperse the matter. Most stars have masses ranging between one-half and four times the mass of the Sun. Greater masses

The North America nebula in Cygnus. A concentration of thin gases which are stirred up as in a neon tube.

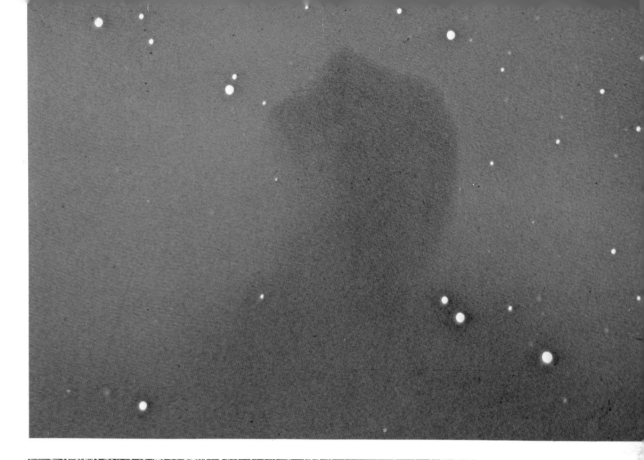

The Horse's Head (or Horsehead) nebula. It obscures the light of the star and nebula lying behind it.

An S-shaped nebula obscures partially or totally the light of the star lying behind.

Opposite: *The Trifid nebula in the Marksman. A shimmering cloud of gas 20,000 million million kilometres (12,500 million million miles) away. Like all galactic nebulae, this is a birthplace of stars.*

53

occur but they are rare. It is significant that the theoretical calculations differ remarkably from observational evidence. There are some unanswered questions here.

The most massive star known is to be found in the constellation of the Swan (Cygnus) and has a mass six hundred times greater than that of the Sun. Still greater masses are scarcely possible since the star would be so hot, and possess such an intense amount of radiation, that its radiation pressure (a force exerted by all forms of radiation) would outweigh the force of its gravity in the outer layers of the star and so prevent the inflow of further matter.

The concentrations of interstellar matter can therefore only be the first stage in the formation of a star. But they are often visible as irregular veil-like or cloud-like formations if they are illuminated by neighbouring stars. Sometimes they are black clouds when they obscure the stars which lie behind them.

Galactic nebulae

These clouds of interstellar matter are the so-called "galactic nebulae" and generally contain more than a thousand times the mass of the Sun, with a general density of around 100 atoms per cubic centimetre (1,600 atoms per cubic inch). The largest of these is the Great Nebula in Orion which is visible even to the naked eye. The other nebulae are only visible

through a telescope. All the nebulae are given numbers which can be found in catalogues and some of them have names which refer to their shapes, for example North America nebula, Horse's head nebula, Rosette nebula and Elephant's trunk nebula.

In these nebulae the evolutionary processes continue and local concentrations of matter are formed. This results in the break-up of the nebula into smaller clouds. The process is generally repeated until each individual concentration of gas and dust contains a quantity of matter several times the mass of the Sun, with densities which may reach 10,000 atoms per cubic centimetre (160,000 atoms per cubic inch). At this point they occupy such a relatively small volume of space that they do not decay as a result of the dispersal of the particles of which they are composed. Gravity is now the dominant force and overrides the forces which lead to dispersal. They assume a generally spherical form and become visible in the galactic nebulae as small, mostly round, dark clouds, called "globules". This is the earliest stage at which nascent stars become visible.

If these considerations are correct then stars are not normally born singly but in groups or "star clusters". Indeed we find that new stars are not evenly distributed in space, but the newer they are the more clearly they form groups called clusters. Some thirty of these are known and traces of nebulae are generally also to be found. The best known example of such a cluster with the remains of a nebula is the Pleiades in the constellation of Taurus. It is generally assumed that the nebulae we have described are the birth-places of the stars.

Within the globules the process of condensation continues under the

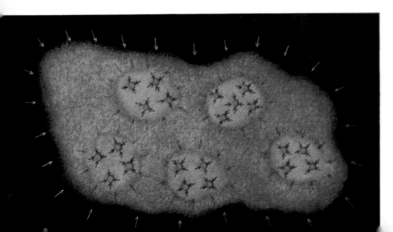

Opposite: *The Sun is a huge sphere of burning gases 1,392,489 kilometres (870,305 miles) in diameter. Its mass is 333,000 times that of Earth.*

The Pleiades in Taurus. A cluster of young stars with remains of the nebula from which they were created.

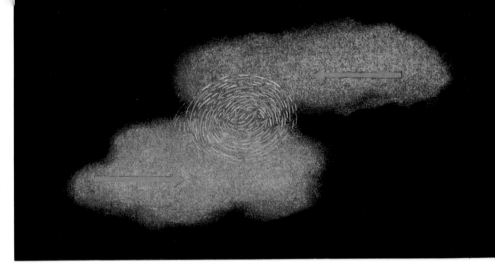

influence of gravitational forces, and this has two consequences. When a volume of gas condenses, rotational movement which is already in existence is accelerated according to the principle of conservation of the rotational momentum. This is the same principle used by the ice-skater in a pirouette—by drawing in his arms he achieves a faster rate of spin. It can safely be assumed that there are rotational currents in the nebulae. These occur wherever the great clouds of intersteller matter which form the nebulae make tangential contact with each other, rather than collide directly. The former appears to prevail, and so each nebula and its component parts are given a certain rotational movement. This rotation is accelerated when a globule within the nebula condenses further to form a star. This is why most new stars (novae) rotate at high speed.

The effects of rapid rotation are that generally only the inner part of the globule condenses further to form a star, while the outer part is prevented from doing so by centrifugal force. This results in a flat disc forming round the star, which rotates like Saturn's ring system.

A further consequence of the rapid rotation of the globule is that the gases become hot. This increase in temperature is the result of rising pressures in the core of the globule,

and is similar to the heat produced when pressures rise in a bicycle pump during the inflation of a tyre. In the globule the temperatures can be very high due to the enormous pressures. During the early stages of condensation there were comparatively minor increases in temperature. However, the heat was diffused by radiation because of the generally low density of the matter. In the globule this can no longer take place and the heat builds up in the core. At first the star begins to glow dimly and then to shine more brightly with the steadily rising temperature. When the temperature in the core has reached 5 million °C (9 million °F), nuclear reactions begin. The nuclear reactions create extraordinary amounts of energy, forcing the temperatures even higher. At the incredible temperature of 14 million °C (25 million °F), energy generation proceeds at its fullest. The star is ablaze and mature.

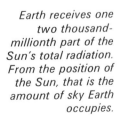

into space the astonishing amount of $370,000 \times 10^{18}$ kilowatts of energy. Earth only absorbs one two thousand millionth part of this energy because, seen from the Sun, this is the small part of space that Earth occupies. However, this small proportion represents 185×10^{12} kilowatts or 50,000 million kilowatt-hours per second, which is more than two million times the energy requirements of the world at present.

Star formation

The steps in the formation of stars are:

1. Stars are formed from diffuse interstellar matter comprising gas and dust.
2. This matter condenses (under suitable conditions) to form galactic nebulae.
3. These nebulae are concentrated, often through repeated processes and form globules.
4. These latter concentrations have high internal pressures which create high temperatures and from a steady escalation of the temperature under gravitational forces, nuclear energy generation is set in motion.

The steps outlined above apply equally to our Sun because it is not a special case requiring a different explanation. It is a star similar to many millions in our galaxy.

The Sun continuously radiates

Source of energy

In the past the source of this energy caused great difficulties. Many different possibilities were considered. These included the burning of $7,000 \times 10^{12}$ tons of coal a second, and a rain of 300×10^{12} goods trains full of meteorites per second on to the Sun's surface. Finally it was suggested that there must be a fuel with an extraordinary energy content in the Sun, in fact a fuel which was unknown on Earth. Then, with the fission of uranium by the German physicists Otto Hahn and Fritz Strassmann in 1939, the answer to the question of the Sun's source of energy was found. Now we know the types of reactions and processes at work in the heart of the Sun.

Hydrogen is being transformed into helium in the Sun, and this change is a process which we are able to reproduce here on Earth, in the form of a hydrogen-bomb explosion. This reaction produces vast amounts of energy which many men are striving to control and tame for peaceful purposes because it would free us from all our worries about meeting future demands for energy. The great difficulties involved lie in the control of the extremely high pressures and the temperatures which are an integral part of the process.

The stars are vast nuclear reactors

The Sun's energy is created in its core at a temperature of 16 million °C (61 million °F) by a process which transforms hydrogen into helium. As a result an increasing quantity of helium is accumulating at the Sun's core.

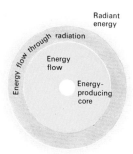

Radiant energy

Energy flow through radiation

Energy flow

Energy-producing core

where the high pressures and temperatures are controlled essentially by the force of gravitation and, in the case of the Sun, by its distance from Earth.

Calculations indicate that there

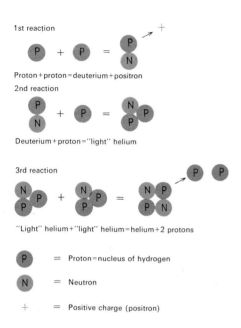

1st reaction

Proton + proton = deuterium + positron

2nd reaction

Deuterium + proton = "light" helium

3rd reaction

"Light" helium + "light" helium = helium + 2 protons

P   = Proton = nucleus of hydrogen

N   = Neutron

+   = Positive charge (positron)

are pressures of the order of 2·2 × 10¹¹ atmospheres and temperatures of about 15 million °C (27 million °F) in the core of the Sun. The very high pressure results in the great concentration of atoms (one cubic centimetre on the Sun contains 134 grams of matter; one cubic inch contains 4·7 pounds), while the very high temperature produces their violent movement. Under these particular conditions there are many violent collisions of the atoms with the result that helium is built up from hydrogen atoms by means of the proton-proton reaction.

The proton is the positively charged nucleus of the hydrogen atom, which is the building brick in the process described. The process proceeds as follows: the first step in the reaction is the combination of two protons (hydrogen nuclei) to

form heavy hydrogen or deuterium. In the course of this reaction a positron is released. The second step occurs when the deuterium nucleus, or heavy hydrogen, collides with another proton to form an isotope of helium with the release of gamma rays. The third and final step consists of the combination of two "light" helium isotopes to form a normal helium nucleus and the release of two protons.

The important point about this combination of atoms is that a substantial quantity of energy is released in the process. If one takes the mass of a proton as 1 then the mass of the helium nucleus should be 4, but in fact it is only 3·97. This means that in the formation of helium from hydrogen a fraction of the matter involved is transformed into energy.

In this process even a relatively small loss of mass releases an enormous amount of energy. If one gram (0·035 ounce) of hydrogen (that is 11 litres or 671 cubic inches at normal atmospheric pressure) is transformed into helium, only 0·0068 gram (0·00024 ounce) of matter is lost, but 170,000 kilowatt-hours of energy are released.

This reaction is the energy source of the Sun and in this way some 564 million tons of hydrogen are transformed into helium every second. The matter that is converted to energy in the process, and is dispersed from the Sun, amounts to four million tons, and the energy generated amounts to 370,000 × 10¹⁸ kilowatts. These amounts are colossal and are difficult to comprehend. But in spite of the fact that they appear enormous to us, they are still relatively insignificant in terms of the Sun itself. Its hydrogen supply is sufficient to maintain its present energy generation at the same level for at least another 5,000 million years.

The Sun derives its energy from the proton-proton reaction. Only nuclei of the atoms are shown.

Opposite: The amount of energy generated by the Sun in one second would be enough to satisfy the power requirements of the whole human race for 140 million years.

CHAPTER 7

THE ORIGIN
OF EARTH

Although we are generally very interested in the origin of the universe, the question which probably fascinates us most is the origin of our own planet Earth.

The planets are the "wandering stars", the celestial bodies which alter their positions in the sky relatively quickly, as opposed to the "fixed stars", the almost imperceptible movements of which can be established only over very long periods of time. The ancients found the movements of the planets so mysterious that they connected them with the will and the moods of the gods. They also named them after some of the gods (Mercury, Venus, Mars, Jupiter and Saturn). This practice has been continued with the more recently discovered planets —Uranus, Neptune and Pluto. Ancient peoples believed that they could interpret the plans and intentions of the gods from the changing positions of the visible planets. This belief still survives in the practice of astrology.

Harmony of the spheres

In reality of course, the movements of the planets in their orbits are certainly not determined by moods or whims, but are governed by rules and laws which are as straightforward and strict as those which control the motions of any other

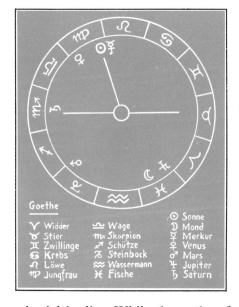

Goethe

♈ Widder	♎ Wage	☉ Sonne
♉ Stier	♏ Skorpion	☽ Mond
♊ Zwillinge	♐ Schütze	☿ Merkur
♋ Krebs	♑ Steinbock	♀ Venus
♌ Löwe	♒ Wassermann	♂ Mars
♍ Jungfrau	♓ Fische	♃ Jupiter
		♄ Saturn

The horoscope of the German poet Goethe. Astrologers believe that the position of the planets at the moment of birth determines a person's character and destiny.

celestial bodies. While the paths of comets and meteors cross each other in an apparently haphazard and confusing manner, throughout the solar system all the planets including Earth move round the Sun in their orbits without exception in strict order, and all in approximately the same plane. This is why they are only to be seen from Earth in a comparatively narrow belt of the night sky, the zone known as the Zodiac. The plane of their orbital paths acquires special significance since it is also the plane of the Sun's equator, that is the plane at right angles to the axis about which the Sun itself rotates.

Opposite: Earth— seen here from the Moon—"belongs" to the planets, is a "companion" of the Sun and can only have originated with the Sun.

Furthermore, the planets travel in almost concentric circles and in the same direction round the Sun. This is in the same direction as the Sun rotates. The planets too rotate

in accordance with Bode's Law.

It is inconceivable that such orderly relationships could have come about by pure chance. So any attempt to explain the origin of the

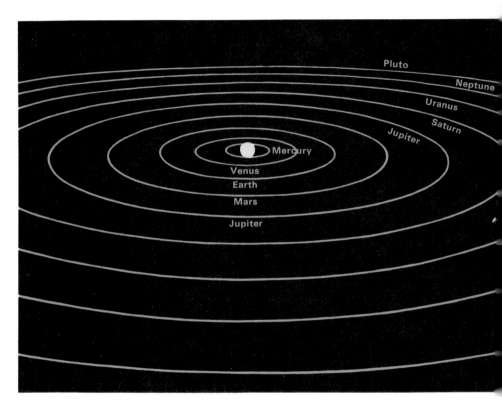

4,498 — Neptune

2,872 — Uranus

1,428 — Saturn

778 — Jupiter

228 — Mars
150 — Earth
108 — Venus
58 — Mercury

in the same direction and, if they have genuine moons, these also follow the same rule. Finally, the distances between the planets obey Bode's Law which was mentioned in Chapter 4.

The orderliness is very impressive and it suggested to the Greek philosopher Pythagoras the image of "the harmony of the spheres". The planets were considered to be fixed to crystal spheres that revolved round Earth (which was considered to be the focus). Men believed that, just as in music, the harmonic intervals are dependent upon simple length relationships in a taut string, so the spheres which bore the planets sang in cosmic harmony. In fact, the planets all revolve in their orbits

planets must start from the idea that they were not captured by the Sun but are intimately related to it. They either originated from the Sun itself or were formed in very close association with it.

We now encounter a difficulty, because the planets differ markedly from the Sun in their material composition. Whereas in the Sun we find 99 per cent hydrogen and helium with only 1 per cent heavier elements, in the planets we find virtually only the latter. In spite of the tremendous impression that the great expanses of the oceans make upon us, and in spite of the further wide distribution of hydrogen in all forms of life and in minerals, the element hydrogen constitutes only 0·003 per cent of the Earth's weight. The proportion of helium amounts to perhaps only one thousand millionth part of one per cent. The planets Mercury, Venus and Mars fall into the same category as Earth, and are composed mainly of heavy elements, while the larger planets Jupiter, Saturn, Uranus and Neptune possess perhaps considerably more hydrogen, but the amount is not really significant. Not enough is known about the planet Pluto. How can this major difference in composition between the Sun and the planets be explained?

Formation of planets

It is now assumed that the planets are remnants of an earlier phase in the Sun's development. We have discussed previously the characteristics of hot new stars which have just developed from globules in the nebulae and how they are surrounded by a flattened disc of interstellar matter. They are huge, white-hot spheres of gas often having outer "atmospheres" with rotational speeds of up to 300 kilometres (186 miles) per second, compared with 2 kilometres (1·2 miles) per second in the case of the Sun. In this early stage they are very close to the limit where centrifugal force would tear them apart. This rapid rotation probably explains why the disc remains intact instead of collapsing into the star.

Both the star and the disc consist, like the interstellar matter from which they were formed, of 99 per cent hydrogen and helium with 1 per cent of heavier elements. In the actual star all the matter is in a gaseous state due to the tremendously high temperatures. In the disc however, as in the clouds of interstellar matter, the heavier elements remain in the form of finely divided dust, because the tempera-

tures are much lower. Hydrogen and helium remain in a gaseous state even under these conditions since they liquefy only under extremely high pressures.

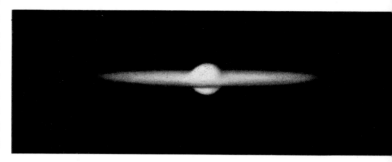

Let us now consider the disc composed of gas and dust. We have already discussed the properties and characteristics of a disc made up of particles, and we have seen that it does not revolve uniformly as a solid entity. In fact, the speed of rotation of the disc must be different at varying distances from the Sun at the centre, that is it revolves more slowly far from it and faster closer to it. Under these conditions the gases and solid components of the disc behave differently.

Below: *A young star surrounded by a flat disc of interstellar matter from which, it is thought, stars are formed.*

Opposite left: *The distance of the various planets from the Sun increases according to a regular law.*
Opposite right: *All planets travel almost exactly in concentric orbits and in the same plane round the Sun.*

Below: *There are many eddies and vortices in the disc round the Sun.*

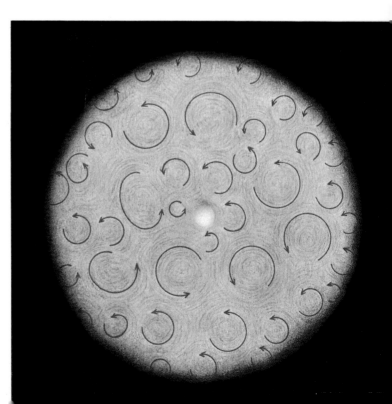

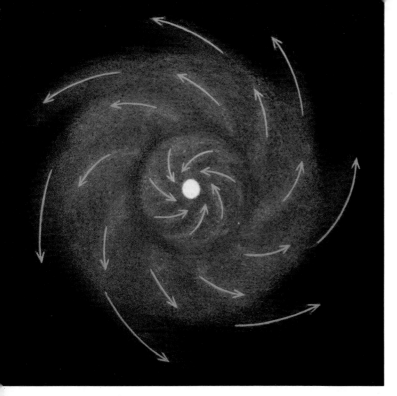

The disc loses its
gaseous constituents
when the balance
between centrifugal
force and
gravitational pull is
disturbed.

slowing down its rotation. In the outer regions on the other hand, where the rate of rotation is greater, centrifugal force is dominant and overcomes the gravity of the star with the result that matter is dispersed into space.

Calculations have been made which demonstrate that the mass of matter making up the disc, which after all is 99 per cent gas, is reduced by half in this way every five million years. The bulk of the gaseous constituents of the disc will be effectively dispersed within a period of 200 million years.

What happens to the solid constituents of the disc? Since they are single particles or very small, non-cohesive, independent grains which describe a multiplicity of vaguely circular orbits round the star without exerting any reciprocal influence on each other as the concentrations of gas did, they tend to behave in a rather different way. If the particles are very small they are carried along by the gas currents, and like the gas are involved in the vortices and are eventually lost in space along with the gaseous constituents of the disc. In spite of this loss, the eddies and swirls in the clouds of gas also cause countless contacts and collisions between the dust particles. If two particles meet they are held together by their (admittedly small) mass attraction and in time thus form ever larger accumulations of particles with resulting stronger gravitational attraction. In this way, ever greater agglomerations of solid matter are built up by accretion, and these follow the currents and vortices in the gas clouds to a diminishing extent until they orbit the Sun on their specific, nearly circular paths with ever increasing consistency. It probably takes only a short time, possibly a few thousand years, until they are of sufficient size to

In the first place the gases expand, are widely distributed and form a single but very loosely cohesive disc-shaped cloud. The belts of matter which rotate at different speeds influence each other where they come in contact, and currents of gas which move at different speeds give rise to turbulence wherever they meet or adjoin. As a result the disc is affected by vortices created by the turbulence. These vortices produce a continual exchange of matter between the different zones of the cloud. Fast-moving concentrations pass from the inner to the outer parts of the disc and accelerate the rotation, whereas the slow-moving concentrations of matter move inwards and tend to slow down the rotation there. Thus in all parts of the disc the balance between the gravity of the star and the centrifugal force which is produced by its rotation, so crucial to the maintenance of the existing state, is profoundly disturbed.

In the inner regions where the rate of rotation is too slow, gravity is dominant and this results in quantities of matter falling into the star and

Opposite: *The
relative sizes of the
planets.*

determine their own orbital paths.

Once this is the case and they are established in their orbits, they can no longer be carried off into space by the escaping currents of gas. In fact the gas clouds constantly supply them with new particles which either collide directly with them or are swept up by them because of their increasing gravitational attraction. As a result of this sweeping action they virtually clear the space in their immediate vicinity of solid particles and build up a few large concentrations of matter. The time it takes for the gas cloud to disperse is considered sufficient to allow concentrations of matter to develop which are of planet size.

The original mass of the disc was approximately equivalent to the mass of the Sun, and only one per cent of that consists of heavier elements. It can be assumed that the bulk of the solid constituents of the disc were lost with the dispersal of the gas so that only a very small part remained. In fact the total mass of all the planets is equal to only one seven hundredth part of the Sun's mass.

The Sun, however, retained its proportion of the hydrogen and helium in the original gas cloud and, if in the early stages of its existence it rotated more quickly, it was later slowed down to such an extent by the slower-moving masses falling into it from the disc, that at this present stage of its history the Sun rotates only comparatively slowly.

If we accept that these are the processes which produced the evolving solar system, then we can consider that they also provide explanations of the following phenomena:
1. The position of the planetary orbits on the plane of the Sun's equator.
2. The shape of the planetary paths round the Sun (almost concentric circles).

3. The coincidence of all orbiting directions and most rotational directions with the direction of rotation of the Sun.
4. The distribution of mass in the solar system between the planets and the Sun in the ratio of 1:700.
5. The differences of material composition between the Sun and the planets. In the Sun hydrogen and helium are dominant, while in the planets there are almost exclusively heavier elements with only a very small percentage of hydrogen and helium.

It can be assumed with some confidence that these are the processes which formed the planets. They developed from a cold cloud of interstellar matter which encircled the youthful Sun in the form of a disc and so the planets were presumably not at first molten. That some of them are hot in the central regions today, if we can take the situation found within Earth as a guide, can be traced back to subsequent heating up produced by heat energy given off by the decay of radio-active elements within Earth. It should be considered a distinct possibility that in the case of the asteroids, the primeval matter in the disc condensed to form several small bodies rather than one large one. If this were the case the asteroids developed directly from accretion of dust particles and were not created from the destruction of a larger planet. In Chapter 4, however, we have set out the reasons which led us to accept the alternative mode of origin.

The moons of Jupiter and Saturn which we discussed in Chapter 5, and also the five moons of Uranus, which all orbit exactly on the plane of each planet's equator, could also possibly have developed like the planets themselves from a nebular disc which surrounded their respective mother planets. These very

Much of Earth's landscape is characterized by varied physical features—the green of plants and trees, and the blue of the sky overhead.

large planets all rotate very quickly, in about ten hours, so that similar conditions could have existed in the case of each of these planets and their moons as that which occurred for the Sun and the planets.

Earth originated just like the other planets when the Sun was a young star, except that in this case there is a slight peculiarity, because two bodies rather than one were formed. These are Earth and the Moon—one large, the other small.

The distinctive appearances of the two bodies can be explained by the difference in their masses. The gravitational attraction of the Moon (which we already know is a sixth of Earth's) is so weak that it could not retain an atmosphere. Gases are composed of rapidly moving molecules which tend to spread out into space, and will continue to disperse unless they are restrained by strong gravitational forces, or are dense gases with a high molecular weight.

meteorites that throughout its history has turned its surface into a dust-covered crater-landscape. On Earth the smaller meteors do not reach the surface because they burn up high in the atmosphere, and the effects of the meteorites when they hit the land masses and not the sea, are soon obliterated by the active weathering processes.

On the Moon, however, the bare primeval rock is exposed, whereas on Earth it has been eroded by various agents, carried down to the sea by rivers or ice and deposited in

It is probable, therefore, that the Moon lost all the gases it may have possessed, if indeed it possessed any, including water vapour which, after hydrogen and helium, is the lightest and therefore the most easily dispersed gas. As a result of the loss of the gases the Moon lacks everything the atmosphere and water have created on Earth—the land and sea, rivers and lakes, clouds, rain, weathering and life. The Moon is helplessly exposed to the rain of

layers often of great thickness, only to be raised up again in the form of mountains where the processes of destruction begin again. The transformation of the original rocks into many types of stratified sedimentary rocks by repeated erosion and redeposition has resulted in the burial of the original crystal rocks. The newer sedimentary rocks with their different colours and textures give Earth's surface its varied topography and often distinctive colours.

The landscape of the Moon consists of craters and bare rock. The sky is always black.

None of this exists on the Moon.

Life on other planets

One of the most fascinating questions which is asked, is whether there are other planets apart from Earth which sustain life in some form or other, or even act as homes for some kind of rational beings.

First, let us assume that life can originate wherever conditions are favourable. Life is very complex and delicate and is characterized by a multitude of rapid chemical reactions and combinations which, as we have already observed, are dependent on the presence of water, without which life in the sense of the organisms we know on Earth is impossible.

Life demands temperatures which fall within a specific range, that is they are not permanently above the boiling-point of water or below the freezing-point. A suitable environment is also required in which all the necessary materials are available. In terms of the cosmos, however, this temperature range is extremely restricted and even on Earth these conditions exist only within certain comparatively narrow latitudinal and altitudinal zones. As far as we can determine, temperatures like those found on Earth are not likely to prevail on other planets within the solar system. To take an example, the temperature on Mercury reaches 400 °C (720 °F) on the side facing the Sun, and on Jupiter, and more especially the more distant planets, temperatures of less than −100 °C (−148 °F) have been measured. These temperatures mean that life as we know it cannot exist and these planets can be eliminated from our list of those that may support some form of life. A planet must lie at precisely the right distance from the Sun otherwise life cannot exist on it, because it is either too hot or too cold.

In the case of the planet Mars, the average temperature on the illuminated side is −15 °C (5 °F), but the temperature rises around midday to 10° or even 20 °C (50° or 68 °F). As far as temperature is concerned, therefore, there is the possibility that some very resistant life form could exist on that planet. Recent space probes which have photographed the surface of the planet have, however, sent back pictures which tend to discourage the idea that even some form of primitive vegetation may exist on the surface.

Recent temperature measurements on Venus have shown that there are extremely high temperatures (up to 300 °C or 636 °F) on the surface of the planet accompanied by high atmospheric pressures, so the existence of life as we know it is inconceivable there.

We also know that plants and animals are extremely sensitive to, and have a delicate dependence upon, external environmental conditions—climate, the nutritional possibilities of a region or a locality,

Rock with lichen. On Mars there may be vegetation consisting of mosses and lichens.

the type of soil and the topographic position, among other factors. Even minor climatic changes or subtle chemical changes in the environment can lead to the extinction of entire species. Consequently, we cannot expect to find the same life forms and species on other planets as we find here on Earth, even if life in *some* form is possible. Life may exist, but only in other forms and it is extremely doubtful if conditions identical to those on Earth will be found anywhere within our solar system. In the case of Mars, conditions are so different from those on Earth that familiar terrestrial forms could not possibly exist there. At best from the information available at present, it is considered that the type of life which could exist on Mars would be vaguely similar to the mosses and lichens found in the arctic regions of Earth.

It follows then that within our solar system there are no human beings or even anthropoid life forms except on Earth. The only planet which may have some primitive

form of plant life, apart from Earth, is Mars. Under these circumstances, the problem of whether there are other planets in the universe similar to Earth is important if we wish to answer the question of whether there is likely to be extra-terrestrial life.

If our solar system is regarded as unique because of the manner of its formation, then there are no other such planets in the universe. Nor can there be life on the stars because they are not solid bodies and have surface temperatures of many thousands of degrees. One theory of the origin of the planets which was favoured in the past was that they were created when another star passed very close to the Sun—so close in fact that the passing star tore an enormous strip of matter from the Sun, from which the planets were then formed. If this theory is accepted, then the planets would be the most improbable bodies in the universe, because as we saw in Chapter 6, the stars are, in proportion to their size, as distant from each other as cherries at intervals of 1,000 kilometres (620 miles). The average speed at which they move (when scaled down to the model we present) would amount to only four metres (thirteen feet) in a year. In spite of their enormous numbers, in our part of the galaxy at least, collisions or close approaches between stars are practically impossible.

If however, our explanation for the origin of the planets is accepted, then it is a completely normal process and most stars will have their own group of satellites round them, unless certain exceptional circumstances prevent this happening.

There is a strong probability that planets similar to Earth exist in other solar systems and the possibility of life elsewhere in the universe becomes plausible. It has been

Proconsul. Man looked something like this 20 million years ago. If the total age of Earth were condensed into one year, that length of time represents two days.

Australopithecus. This is approximately how man looked one million years ago. If the total age of Earth were taken as one year, that length of time represents two hours.

calculated that there are 100,000 million planets in the universe similar to Earth. Traces of organic matter have been recorded from certain types of meteorites, but there is still dispute over its source.

Other life forms

We must appreciate that human beings, in terms of the immense periods of time that we are discussing, have only been in existence on Earth for a very short time, for a moment in the history of the universe. If the age of Earth, which is now considered to be in excess of 4,000 million years, is scaled down to a period of a year, then the first, scarcely human ancestors of man appeared late on 31st December, in fact only two hours before the end of the year. Modern man appeared only seven minutes before midnight. The 5,000 years of man's recorded history are equivalent to the last forty seconds of the year.

Man therefore could be seen as the most recent of a series of life forms which have developed during the past 1,000 million years, and he has been in existence for only a brief part of that time. His actual origin, according to contemporary opinion, was the consequence of a series of irregular climatic changes in Africa during the last few million years. In other words, man is the product of special, perhaps unique, influences.

If follows that if another planet is to be the home of similar beings it must have had an almost identical history to that of Earth. It would have to have originated in a similar way and developed similar conditions of life with a similar distribution of continents and oceans. In addition, climatic conditions and cosmic influences such as radiation, which can produce genetic mutations, would have to be alike.

Given the vast number of planets which are believed to exist in the universe, it is admittedly possible that somewhere these conditions could exist. However, it must remain unlikely, or less probable, than the existence of life of some other sort, that is life in a very different form from anything we know.

If interstellar space could be crossed quickly, and if we could reach such a planet, we would in all probability find some form of life, but its aspects would probably be as alien to us as some of the strange creatures of past ages, like those for instance during the Mesozoic era when the dinosaurs roamed Earth, or the early Palaeozoic era when there were no land animals but the sea was teeming with life.

most of them. Can we believe that beings, with a technology vastly superior to our own, would travel distances far in excess of 30,000 million kilometres (19,000 million miles) only to return to their home planet when within short range of their objective? It is very unlikely but the possibility cannot be ignored.

Many interesting ideas have been proposed for establishing radio contact with other beings of an equivalent or higher level of intelligence and development. Several attempts have been made and are in fact in progress. Even if these initial attempts should lead to successful contact, it would be a long time before any profitable exchange of ideas could be made.

These creatures lived on Earth during the Jurassic era, 150 million years ago. 1. Brontosaurus (up to 18 metres (58 feet) in length). 2. Pteranodon (8 metres (26 feet) span). 3. Stegosaurus (up to 9 metres (30 feet) high). 4. Tyrannosaurus (14 metres (45 feet)).

Contact with other worlds

Other solar systems are so distant from ours that a space-craft which can travel to the Moon from Earth (about 384,000 kilometres, 239,000 miles) in sixty-seven hours and fifteen minutes would require 850,000 years to journey to the nearest star. There are several theoretical schemes, it is true, which have suggested how this difficulty might be overcome, but to realize any of them would involve a much greater technology and much more sophisticated methods than we have at our disposal at present or in the foreseeable future. It is possible, of course, that if the life forms on our hypothetical planet were technically more advanced than we are, they might already have developed a way of visiting us.

We might ask: Have we not been visited already? What about "flying saucers"? These unidentified flying objects have been studied very carefully for a number of years and there are sound scientific explanations for

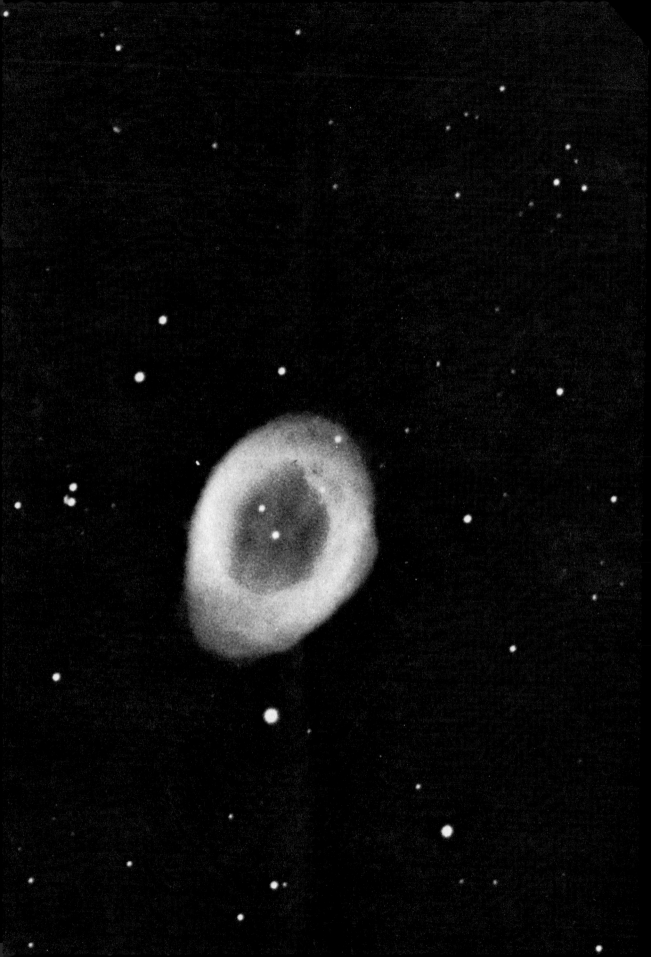

CHAPTER 8

HOW STARS
AGE AND DIE

In Chapter 6 we showed that everything we can observe in the stars gives us valuable information about the evolution of the Sun. Our observations provide a considerable volume of data and at present we have reached a stage where the measurements of such properties as brightness, size, temperature, composition and mass provide a basis for classifying the stars into various groups or types. For classifications we are looking for stable relationships between the quantities we have determined, in other words, consistent patterns that can be applied to the phenomena we record so that we can attempt to understand them.

Relationships and patterns

We can study the differences in size, mass, temperature and brightness to see if they fall into a particular pattern, and then ask whether stars of a similar mass have roughly similar temperatures. If such relationships can be established it is then possible to determine an evolving pattern. In other words, are the sizes of the stars we measure related to different stages in their evolution, or do they correspond to differences of mass, which are the result of condensation from gas clouds of different masses? Some features of the pattern suggest that they are related to the stage of evolution, and that

others are the result of the mass of the original cloud of gas.

Our present mathematical ability and knowledge of the structure of matter enable us to understand and follow the theory behind the conditions and processes that occur in the central regions of a star. The various types are then arranged in such a way that the sequence is related to these ideas and suggest a probable evolutionary development.

The most important relationship —and one which has given very useful results—is the connection between surface temperature and the absolute brightness of the stars.

Opposite: The Ring nebula in Lyra was formed from the explosion of a star.

Towards the end of its life, the Sun will expand. Within a few million years it will be as big as Aldebaran in Taurus and will occupy as much of Earth's sky as the constellation Orion.

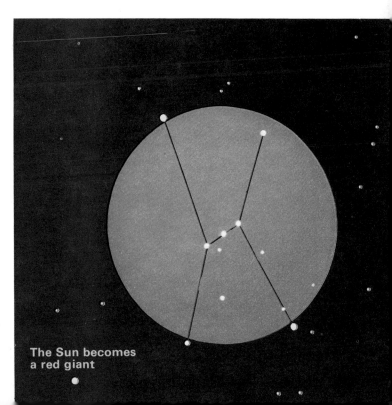

The Sun becomes
a red giant

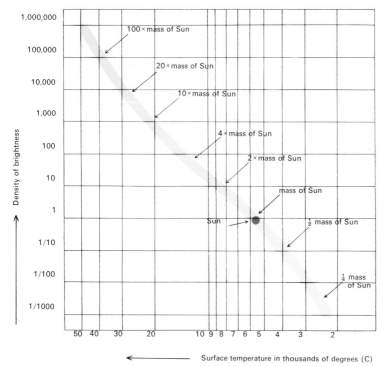

Density of brightness

1,000,000
100,000
10,000
1,000
100
10
1
1/10
1/100
1/1000

100 × mass of Sun

20 × mass of Sun

10 × mass of Sun

4 × mass of Sun

2 × mass of Sun

mass of Sun

Sun

½ mass of Sun

¼ mass of Sun

50 40 30   20   10 9 8 7 6 5   4   3   2

Surface temperature in thousands of degrees (C)

The Hertzsprung-Russell diagram.

This is represented by the Hertzsprung–Russell diagram named after two astronomers, one Danish the other American, who discovered this relationship independently. In this diagram the great majority of stars (including the Sun) are to be found within a narrow band which is called the "main sequence". There is a uniform relationship between the surface temperature and brightness, in other words stars are corre-

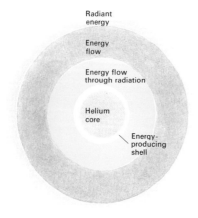

Radiant energy

Energy flow

Energy flow through radiation

Helium core

Energy-producing shell

The structure of a red giant. The core is composed of helium. Hydrogen is transformed into helium only in a shell round the core.

spondingly hotter when there is an increase in their total radiation and mass.

Main sequence stars

It is generally accepted today that every star begins its existence as a main sequence star, and its temperature is higher and it radiates greater quantities of energy with every increase in the mass from which it developed. The other rarer types of stars recorded in the diagram represent other, later, stages of development and are given special names which accord with their distinctive appearance. These are white dwarfs, red giants, blue giants and super giants. Since the Sun is a main sequence star, these other types can indicate to us something about its future development.

The physical properties of a star, that is its mass, internal pressure, internal temperature, energy generation and radiation, diameter and surface area, are all interrelated. If for example, the energy generated in the core of a star were greater than the radiated energy, then the overall temperature of the star would rise, and there would be an increase in internal pressure, with a resultant expansion of the star and the creation of a greater surface area which could radiate more energy. In this way a new state of balance, even if only temporary, would be achieved.

This balance also means that a main sequence star tends to be very stable, and it does not change very significantly or abruptly throughout the greater part of its existence. The nuclear reactions which produce helium from hydrogen continue steadily in the core. Since the supply of hydrogen is consumed only very slowly (in terms of the total supply available), many stars, in fact the

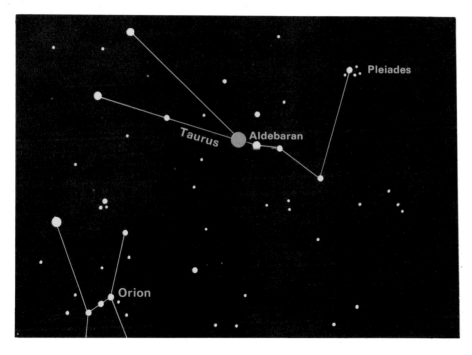

Aldebaran in Taurus is a red giant.

majority, remain in this stable condition for most of their existence. This is one of the principal reasons why main sequence stars constitute the vast majority of those observed.

During the course of time, however, a steadily increasing core of helium is formed, which, when it reaches 12 per cent of the total mass, gradually changes the balance of physical states within the star. The focus of energy generation is displaced from the core to form a shell which surrounds the core. The shell steadily increases in size and the star expands slowly to many times its original diameter. Gradually the brightness of the star decreases, its light becomes redder as the increasing surface area exceeds the energy generation. As the surface area cools it emits a redder light and the star develops into a red giant.

Red giants

Aldebaran, the brightest star in Taurus, is a typical red giant, which is thirty six times larger than the Sun and has one thousand three hundred times the surface area. The temperature at the surface of this enormous star is less than that of the Sun; it is only 3,600 °C (6,480 °F) compared with an upper limit of about 5,700 °C (10,260 °F) on the Sun. If Aldebaran were to replace the Sun in our solar system it would occupy an area of sky equivalent to that outlined by the seven brightest stars in the constellation of Orion.

The development of a red giant involves a process of steady expansion until the original main sequence star has swollen to two or three

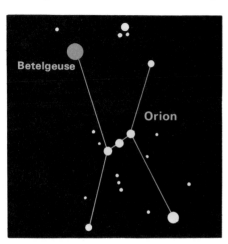

Betelgeuse in Orion is 300 times the size of the Sun and displays irregular fluctuations in brightness.

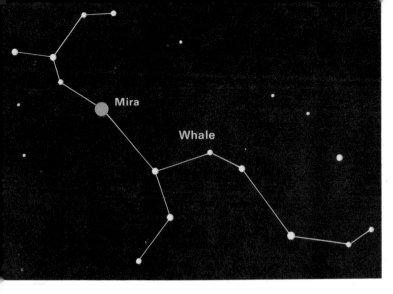

Mira

Whale

served. This is Mira ("the wonderful") the brightness of which varies over a period of on average 320 days in a ratio of 1 : 30.

We know some 1,400 of these giant red stars with brightnesses that fluctuate occasionally, together with

"Light" helium + helium = beryllium

Mira in the constellation Cetus varies regularly in brightness over a period of 320 days.

Right: The synthesis of beryllium from helium. Heavier elements are synthesized at the higher temperatures in the hearts of stars.

hundred times its original diameter. Meanwhile the surface temperature is steadily reduced to around 3,000 °C (5,400 °F) and the star glows red. A typical representative of this group of stars is Betelgeuse in Orion, which is three hundred times bigger than the Sun.

Red giants reveal certain variations in brightness from time to time which represent significant changes of state. These occur at such a rate that they can be directly observed. This is a feature which contrasts vividly with their previous quiescent stage in the main sequence category. During that phase of their development the stars were constant, with significant changes taking place only after the lapse of many millions of years. So a star in the red giant category is unstable and at some point during this stage of its development, a critical state is reached with drastic changes taking place.

A red giant in the constellation Cetus was the first in which a significant change in brightness was ob-

around 1,700 that reveal the initial stages of a certain regularity in their brightness fluctuation. There are a further 3,700 known in which the brightness varies regularly over a period ranging between 80 and 1,000 days. It is probable that these three types are part of an evolutionary pattern, with a sequence which ranges from initially rare variations in brightness through a stage when the frequency is increased to a final regular short-term variation.

The cause of this development is uncertain, but it is assumed to be connected with the massive increases in temperature that are believed to occur within this type of star. Important changes are suspected which occur rapidly and seem to consume enormous quantities of energy. These changes could produce significant temperature variations and so lead to partial collapse of internal pressure. If this occurs the star would then tend to collapse into itself, regaining pressure, temperature and energy with a temporary return to stability.

When a star with a mass similar to that of the Sun has expanded to two or three hundred times its original diameter, it has temperatures at its centre of around 100 million °C (180 million °F). At this stage in its development a new

The variation in brightness of Mira.

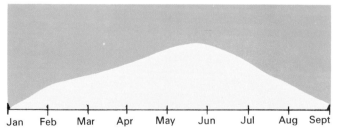

Jan Feb Mar Apr May Jun Jul Aug Sept

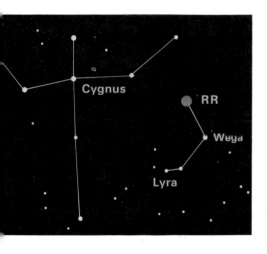

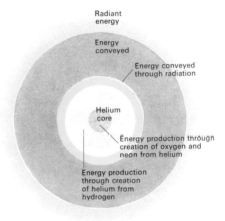

nuclear fusion process begins and helium is transformed into heavier elements. The energy generation within the star is intensified, its surface becomes much hotter again, reaching 20,000 °C (36,000 °F) and more, and the star shines a hundred times more brightly than the Sun.

Pulsating stars

This stage in the development of a star is apparently critical, because variable stars of the RR Lyra type, which are short-period variables or "pulsating stars" possibly produced by exceptionally violent outbursts of energy, appear on the scene. Their sizes change rhythmically and they have a very rapid fluctuation in brightness over periods of between eight and twenty-four hours. Some 2,500 stars of this mysterious type are known, and the causes and processes of the pulsation are still not fully understood.

These stars are extremely valuable because they enable us to measure very great distances in the universe, where most other methods fail. These and the Cepheid stars, another related group of variable stars, reveal that there is an important connection between their absolute brightness and their period of brightness variation. It is possible to deter-mine the absolute brightness of these stars by measuring the period of variation. The comparative distances can then be calculated by comparing the stars' absolute brightness with their apparent brightness.

Novae

It is possible that this rapid pulsation eventually leads directly to the catastrophic destruction of the star. The star effectively breaks up, and in the space of a few hours hurls its outer envelope or layers into space. This is a result of one explosion, or a

Variations in brightness of the star Delta in Cepheus. This is a Cephid variable.

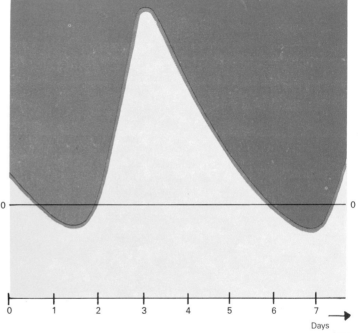

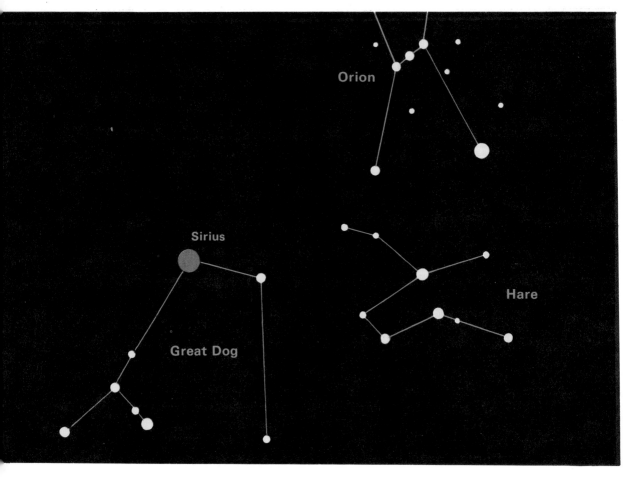

Orion

Sirius

Hare

Great Dog

series of explosions over a period with long intervals between. Finally only the core remains, but it flares up so brightly that the star which had previously been only one among millions now becomes a conspicuously bright object. This has been given the mistaken name of "nova" (new star) because it was formerly considered to be a star appearing from nothing. After the explosion or explosions the matter expelled from the star is dispersed into space and joins the clouds of interstellar matter from which the star, and the others round it, were originally formed.

A typical nova is a star which passes rapidly from an absolute brightness of about thirty times that of the Sun to one of about 100,000 times the Sun's. This is a temporary feature and generally lasts for a comparatively short interval (one or two weeks), after which it fades very quickly. About twenty or thirty of these novae are visible every year.

The remains of these stars, after the colossal dispersal of matter into space, are the white dwarfs, which are as physically distinctive as the red giants. These small stars have diameters of between one-hundredth and one-fiftieth of that of the Sun, that is they are generally about the size of the planet Jupiter. They consist of super dense matter, of which one cubic centimetre weighs a ton (one cubic inch weighs sixteen tons) and they radiate their residual heat into space, the body having a surface temperature of approximately 12,000 °C (21,600 °F).

What eventually happens to the white dwarfs? As yet we do not know. Since energy generation is no longer taking place within them, we assume they must gradually cool down. They probably become fainter and weaker with a redder light and eventually pass into the blackness of space from which they came. This however is a very slow process which presumably takes thousands of millions of years, because their surface areas are so small that they cannot radiate large quantities of energy. What are the prospects for the Sun?

Calculations have been made which suggest that it will be some 4,000 million years before the Sun begins to leave the main sequence of stars. Many things can happen in such an enormous period of time and the question of what happens to man is a purely academic one.

The future development of the Sun displayed in the Hertzsprung-Russell diagram. Main sequence star—red giant—pulsar—nova—white dwarf.

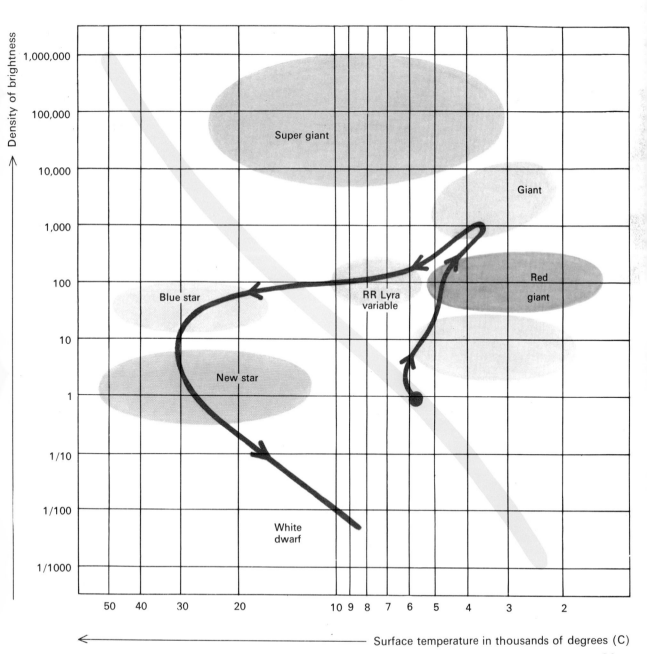

CHAPTER 9

HOW OLD IS
THE UNIVERSE?

It must be made clear that the phrase "I cannot imagine that" is no proof that an idea is wrong. All our ideas are drawn from our knowledge and experience of our environment on Earth. We cannot expect to be in a position to grasp cosmic relationships and cosmic events completely and exactly. Many very familiar everyday phenomena are difficult to grasp. We know, for instance, that a magnet attracts a piece of iron even across a vacuum; but we cannot understand *how* it does it. Nevertheless, there is not the slightest doubt about the fact that it has a power of attraction.

The limitations of our powers of imagination become all the more noticeable the farther we move from the world around us. So we should not expect to have the origin of the universe demonstrated to us like a conjuring trick.

We shall attempt to penetrate, step by step and with the help of analogies, right back to the beginning. If our powers of imagination fail us, then we must be all the more careful not to leave the safe ground of physical certainties. We shall attempt to present the natural world as an event which takes place in time and space, which concerns matter, and in which the driving force is energy in its various forms. Later we shall investigate the idea that matter and energy are not fundamentally different but only different manifestations of the same thing. We shall discuss, therefore, the three basic elements in our world—time, space and matter. And we shall show that matter can be transformed into energy.

What do we know about these three important elements that should help us to make progress in our study?

Time

Let us look first at time. Perhaps one of the surprising things about our present scientific knowledge is that we can provide very precise figures for the age of stars and star-clusters. In earlier times, statements about the age of the world were based on myths and legends or on the words of the Old Testament. Some people went so far in their interpretations of these extremely unreliable sources that, for example, the Irish clergyman James Usher categorically declared in 1654 that the world had been created at 9 o' clock in the morning on 26th October in the year 4004 B.C.

Unfortunately, we cannot be as precise as the Irish bishop, but our figures are better founded. There are various ways of determining the age of the universe and it is a fascinating exercise to compare their results.

The globular star cluster M13 in Hercules is one of the oldest known phenomena in the universe.

Age of the universe

Modern technical equipment enables us to find out about the luminosity, the mass, the state and composition of individual stars in such detail, that it is possible for us to determine their age. The stars examined, which include relatively old stars, have ages that range from 500,000 to 5,700 million years. The most recent investigations lead us to suspect that the upper age limit is in the region of 10,000 million years. Our Sun is estimated to be between 4,700 and 5,000 million years old and so is considered to be in its "middle age".

We find in the sky a large number of "open clusters" of stars in which from twenty to 300 loosely arranged stars obviously form a homogeneous group. From the 400 or so clusters that have been catalogued we estimate that there must be about 15,000 in total. Their ages can be judged not only from the condition of the stars but from their degree of scattering. The stars all attract one another. If two stars pass close enough to each other, both are deflected from their paths. It can happen that one is almost brought to a standstill, while the other flies on twice as fast as before. In the course of time some stars can achieve high speeds in this way and become "rogues". They are lost to the cluster, in which the remaining stars move closer together to compensate. In this way the cluster is broken up and there remains only a very compact group of a few stars.

If one computes these changes, one finds that "open clusters" of stars range between 4·4 and 870 million years old. Three of the clusters examined have an age of over 1,000 million years, and the oldest is 4,600 million years old.

The "galactic clusters" discussed in Chapter 6 are much younger. Their ages lie between half a million and seven million years. Star clusters are known in which many thousands are grouped in a spherical structure. The number of these "globular clusters" is estimated at around 300, of which half are known.

If one examines the stages of development of these stars, a clearly defined limit is revealed at around 1·3 times the mass of the Sun. Above this limit no main sequence stars are found, only giants. That means that all the stars in a globular cluster must have been born at the same time (which its regular structure also leads one to suspect), and that a star leaves the main sequence earlier if its mass is greater than the norm (which is also indicated by mathematical investigations). The more massive the star the more disproportionate the rate of energy loss, and the sooner it leaves the main sequence.

This phenomenon enables us to judge accurately the age of the globular clusters. They are almost universally 6,000 to 7,000 million years old, but according to the latest figures their age could even approach 10,000 million years.

The most reliable dating technique is based on radio-activity. Radio-active matter, such as uranium,

Auriga

AE Aurigae

Gemini

Taurus

Aries

53 Arietis

128 km (79·4 miles) per second

80 km (50 miles) per second

Cetus

Orion

128 km (79·4 miles) per second

Lepus

μ Columbae

Columba

thorium and so on, decays to form other elements with precise known laws. For example, lead is formed from uranium through a series of other elements. So, if we find uranium in a rock, we know that there will always be lead there too. Since we know the rate of decay, we can calculate the age of the rock from the relative proportions of the materials within it. The procedure is still reliable even if there has previously been lead in the rock; for the lead derived from uranium is distinguished from normal lead by a different atomic weight. If this procedure is applied to rocks from Earth's crust, the greatest age yet revealed is 3,700 million years. An age of 3,700 to 4,600 million years

The stars 53 Arietis, AE Aurigae and μ Columbae are rogues. They were originally in the Orion cluster. From the speed and direction of their movement, it has been calculated that they left the cluster between 2·6 and 4·6 million years ago.

was given for samples of Moon-rock. The ages established by this method for meteorites has ranged from sixty to 5,000 million years.

It is interesting to note that irrespective of the methods used, we

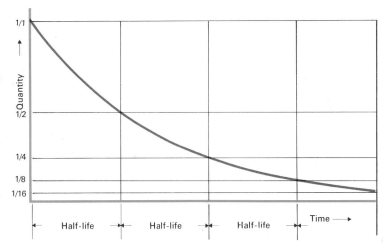

The age of rock containing radioactive elements can be determined because the elements decay in a fixed way. Uranium 238 has a "half-life" of 4,500 million years.

repeatedly arrive at the same greatest age of a few thousand million years. Since each calculation of age was reached by different means, they corroborate each other. The youngest cosmic objects—stars and globular clusters—are less than 500,000 years old and originated (in cosmic terms) in the present, at a time when primitive man already existed on Earth. So the universe is not something changeless, complete or finished, but something that has been forming for thousands of millions of years; and stars are still coming into existence now. No cosmic object has yet been found that is older than 10,000 million years.

Let us postpone, for the moment, the question of whether there could be older objects which we happen not to have found yet. What conclusions can we draw from this figure?

Before this time there can have been no stars, no star-clusters and no solar system. There was nothing apart from the interstellar matter from which the stars were then formed.

However, if this matter is supposed to have existed from infinity, we are faced with the question of why the stars did not begin to develop from it long before they did. Why did they only begin 10,000 million years ago? Because we cannot assume that interstellar matter was always present, with its potential for development, but only became active at that particular time, we suggest that it too must also have come into existence then.

Again, if it only came into existence then, where did it come from? How did it originate? What was there before it, from which it could arise? In other words what happened 10,000 million years ago? Here we are helped, to some extent, by a phenomenon called the "dispersal of the spiral galaxies".

Dispersal of the spiral galaxies

The pale shimmering belt of the Milky Way is seen through a telescope as a dense "snowstorm" of millions and millions of stars. However, their closely packed "density" is an illusion. In reality they are as far apart from each other as are stars anywhere else. The hordes of stars stretch in the plane of the galaxy to such huge distances that there is

hardly a spot in the sky where somewhere, far away, no star is shining.

Outside the Milky Way the stars are arranged in a gigantic lens-shaped structure. It can also be established that although the Sun lies near the central plane of the galaxy, it is not in the centre. Also, the stars do not occupy their lens-shaped position in any regular distribution, but form instead several (probably seven) strips of star cloud that wind in a spiral shape—a Catherine-wheel of unimaginable dimensions, made up of 100,000 million stars, that turns round its focus once in about 230 million years. Seen from Earth, its focus lies in the direction of the constellation Sagittarius.

Inconceivably large as this circle may be in which we find ourselves (the most distant stars are 635,000 million million kilometres or 394,000 million million miles away), nevertheless we remain on a sort of cosmic island. Separated by the enormous distances of completely empty space, we find in the farthest reaches of the universe other such star systems, which we call "spiral galaxies" because of their form. They are often gathered together in clusters of several hundred and their total number is estimated to be more than

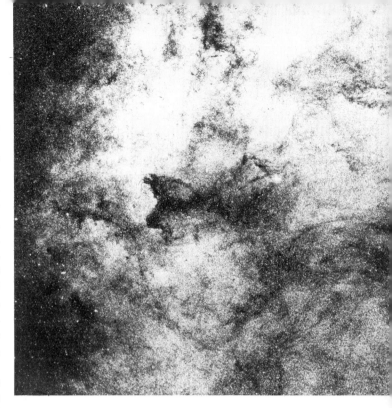

one hundred million. An investigation into the stability of rotating masses has shown that spiral galaxies cannot be older than a few thousand million years.

The spiral galaxies provide us with a clue to the beginning of the universe.

If, with a glass prism or some other equipment, one disperses the light coming from celestial bodies into its constituent colours, one creates the spectrum—a band of colours containing the colours of the rainbow and also numerous fine black absorption lines. These are the absorbed light of certain specific elements and are called Fraunhofer lines after their discoverer, the German optician Joseph von Fraunhofer.

A strange phenomenon is found in the spectra of the spiral galaxies. The characteristic disposition of the Fraunhofer lines remains, but the lines appear shifted farther towards the red end, the more distant the spiral galaxy is from us. What does this red shift mean?

In the Milky Way the stars appear to be so close together that the impression from Earth is of a shimmering screen.

With the use of radiometric dating, the age of meteorites which have reached Earth has been established at about 5,000 million years.

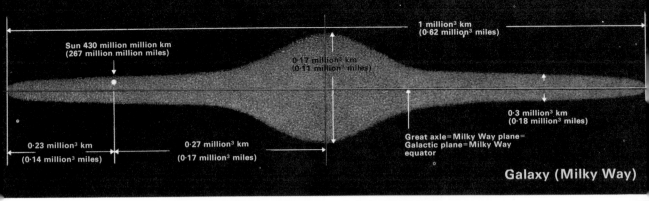

Sun 430 million million km
(267 million million miles)

1 million³ km
(0·62 million³ miles)

0·17 million³ km
(0·11 million³ miles)

0·3 million³ km
(0·18 million³ miles)

Great axle=Milky Way plane=
Galactic plane=Milky Way
equator

0·23 million³ km
(0·14 million³ miles)

0·27 million³ km
(0·17 million³ miles)

Galaxy (Milky Way)

The Sun is far from the centre of the Milky Way but lies near the equatorial plane.

The spiral galaxy in Ursa Major (Great Bear). This is how our galaxy (Milky Way) appears from space.

88

Red shift

We know that the black lines are caused by the presence of certain chemical elements in the atmospheres of stars. Each of these elements extinguishes one or more colours in the spectrum which characterize it.

It is difficult to understand why a chemical element, which can be recognized by its characteristic group of lines, should extinguish increasingly *red* colours the farther away it is from us. The ability to absorb certain colours is built into the structure of its atoms, and that is an unchangeable characteristic of each element. It must be assumed, therefore, that an element always absorbs the same colours, and that the red shift is caused by circumstances which are somehow linked with the distance of the spiral galaxies.

One important physical process is known which could achieve this—the Doppler Effect named after its discoverer, the Austrian physicist Christian Doppler. The effect is revealed by the light radiated from a source being shifted more strongly towards the red side of the spectrum the more quickly the source is receding. This is the same feature that makes the tone of a noise appear deeper the faster it is receding from us. Redder light means a slower rate of oscillation, just as deeper tones indicate slower vibrations.

By observing the red shifts, the speed of recession of the spiral galaxies can be calculated. As a result, surprisingly high speeds stand in a significant relationship to distance. For the spiral galaxies these speeds are respectively 1,200, 15,000, 21,500, 39,000 and 61,000 kilometres (746, 9,320, 13,360, 24,234 and 37,900 miles) per second away from us. The speed of a spiral galaxy is, therefore, greater the farther it is from us. The discovery of this connection we owe to the American astronomer Edwin P. Hubble.

All spiral galaxies are receding from us in every direction. Thus one speaks of the "dispersal of the spiral galaxies". Our galaxy is involved in this dispersal also. If we calculate back into the past, we find that all

The spiral galaxy Andromeda —the nearest to our galaxy.

the spiral galaxies must have started to recede at the same time. This event took place 10,000 million years ago.

So, for yet another reason, we arrive by a completely different path at the same figure for the age of the universe. The question we postponed above, namely whether there could be older objects in the universe which we have not found so far, has been answered. There appear to have been none, for we now know that our present universe most probably began 10,000 million years ago, or that it must at least have been completely different, in so far as anything existed at all before that time.

In the present universe, matter is distributed throughout enormous expanses of space in the form of thousands of millions of stars and galaxies. At a time in the past, however, these individual masses (the total weight of which is reckoned at 7 octillion tons, that is a 7 with 48 noughts, 7×10^{48}) must have been concentrated together in one mighty primeval mass which, if it were placed in the position of the Sun, would not even have reached half-way out to the orbit of Mercury, but a pin-head of this mass would have weighed half a million tons.

This is how our universe might have looked 10,000 million years ago, if we follow familiar ideas. In that case the birth of the universe

Opposite: *The spiral galaxy in Coma Berenices. Seen from the edge, our Milky Way resembles a spindle.* Left: *Spiral galaxies often lie in clusters.* Below left: *Josef von Fraunhofer.* Below: *Spiral galaxies and their spectra (drawn and simplified). The Fraunhofer lines are displaced farther towards the red end of the spectrum, the more distant the spiral galaxy is.*

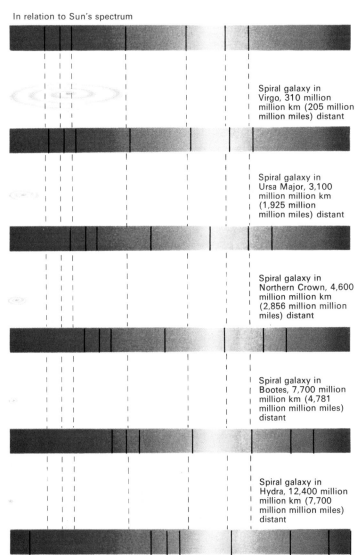

In relation to Sun's spectrum

Spiral galaxy in Virgo, 310 million million km (205 million million miles) distant

Spiral galaxy in Ursa Major, 3,100 million million km (1,925 million million miles) distant

Spiral galaxy in Northern Crown, 4,600 million million km (2,856 million million miles) distant

Spiral galaxy in Bootes, 7,700 million million km (4,781 million million miles) distant

Spiral galaxy in Hydra, 12,400 million million km (7,700 million million miles) distant

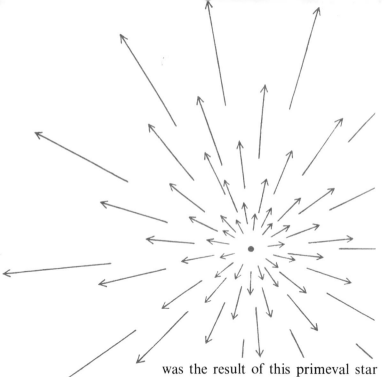

Spiral galaxies are receding from us in all directions. The farther they are from us the greater their speed of recession.

and a thousand million nuclear explosions are nothing compared with the violence of the primeval explosion, but one might ask where did the energy come from, and where did the massive primeval star come from? These two questions demand an answer more urgently than the existence of the thin interstellar matter that was discussed in an earlier chapter.

Energy and the primeval star

Attempts have been made to answer these questions by saying that the great star did not suddenly explode from a previously stable state, but that it arose for a moment from the collapse of an earlier universe and then expanded again immediately like an elastic recoil. The unspoken presupposition of this claim however, is that this collapse brought all the matter of the earlier universe not only to one specific point in space but also at one single point in time. Both of these presumptions are not natural or logical; they represent a contingency of minimal probability, and taken together, they approach impossibility.

What would be the point in answering the question of the origin of the universe with a state or process that combines a maximum of improbability with a minimum of evidence? This does not answer the question; it only pushes it one more unfathomable step back into a nebulous pre-past about which we can now hope to discover nothing; for the question is now: Where did this earlier universe come from? How did it originate?

The dispersal of the spiral galaxies does admittedly reveal to us a guaranteed moment in time for the beginning of our universe, but it still poses (in an even more confused state) the question of the state or

was the result of this primeval star or atom being torn apart by an explosion of inconceivable violence, so that the fragments which attained the highest speeds in the explosion, have meanwhile been dispersed the farthest. That would explain why they are found farther out the greater their speed of flight. The weak point in this picture is, paradoxically, its most spectacular element—the "big bang". We must not allow ourselves to be dazzled by the enormous size of the masses, energies, times and distances of the universe, so that we forget that it also has its limits. The energy discharge is not only of unimaginable proportions but it is too great and therefore impossible. That is to say, the energy discharge that would be necessary to induce speeds (which even today, after 10,000 million years, are still carrying these bodies out into space at 60,000 kilometres (37,000 miles) per second), in a few seconds in a mass of 7 octillion tons, in opposition to the concentrated gravitation of that mass and its gigantic inertia forces would be impossible.

Certainly the image is grandiose

process from which it could have developed.

Perhaps another basic element of our universe will tell us more. Let us now take a look at space.

In previous civilizations the science of astronomy was based simply on measurements of the positions of stars and planets in the heavens using the human eye. The invention of the telescope allowed us to carry out more detailed observations of the skies. However, the human eye is sensitive to only a restricted range of the broad electromagnetic spectrum which extends from gamma radiation emitted by radio-active sources to the kilometre-long waves transmitted by certain radio stations. It was reasonable to assume that stars emit radiation outside the optical range and that such radiation could be detected by suitable radio telescopes. Electro-magnetic radiation can in fact be detected from stars and to a lesser extent from the planets. Radio-astronomy is now a well established science.

One of the best-known radio telescopes is situated at Jodrell Bank in Cheshire, England. This device consists of a large bowl-shaped antenna designed to collect the maximum energy so that it can receive the very weak signals from distant galaxies. The sensitivity of radio telescopes has made them useful to the American and Russian space programmes. The power of the tiny transmitters carried on space vehicles is so low that the signals they transmit to Earth are very weak, especially when the vehicles are very far away from us. For example, the radio signals emitted by the American *Mariner 4* craft were received over a distance of 340 million kilometres (210 million miles), and transmissions were picked up from the Russian *Mars 1* spacecraft when it was 98 million kilometres (61 million miles) from Earth.

It is important to realize that all electro-magnetic radiation, including light and radio waves has a finite velocity of 300,000 kilometres (186,000 miles) per second. This extremely high velocity means that for terrestrial purposes the transmission of information using electromagnetic radiation is virtually instantaneous.

However, when considering interplanetary or interstellar distances, the effect of the speed of light becomes more significant. The time for a beam of light to travel from the Sun to Earth is about eight minutes. The Sun actually goes below our horizon eight minutes before we observe the sunset and rises eight minutes before sunrise.

Once the speed of light was accurately known, astronomers devised a unit of distance which was appropriate to large intergalactic distances—the light year. The light year is simply the distance a ray of light travels in one year and is equal to 9,468 million million kilometres (5,900 million million miles).

CHAPTER 10

HOW BIG
IS SPACE?

In 1826 the German astronomer Heinrich Wilhelm Obers asked: Why is the sky dark at night?

We have seen how, because of the immense expanses of space over which the Milky Way stretches, the stars in it seem to be so densely packed that they melt together in one great, gently shimmering film. If space were infinitely large and uniformly filled with stars and galaxies, then this infinite number of stars would light up the whole sky, as there would ultimately be a star to be seen at every point of the sky. Then the sky would have to be as bright at night as it is during the day.

Finite space

As this is not the case, space cannot be infinitely great, unless of course it is not uniformly populated with stars. However, there is no indication that the distribution of stars is any different in the farthest reaches of space than it is closer to us. And there are good reasons why the average density of matter in space should be the same everywhere. So we are left with the conclusion that space cannot be infinitely great.

Inevitably we are faced with the insoluble problem of what comes beyond space. At once it becomes evident that our powers of imagination are inadequate to answer this, for they are trapped by our limited

concept of space. What could come at the edge of space, if not something else that either is space or occupies space? Can we imagine that the universe is at this point nailed up with planks? Or do we want to agree with the medieval view that space is bordered by a wall behind which Heaven begins? It seems that there can be no answer to the question of the limits of space which does not itself exceed the limits of our powers of imagination.

If we ask a modern physicist whether space is infinite, he too will tell us that there are compelling

A woodcut dating from around 1530. This was the medieval view of Heaven.

Opposite: The sky is dark. Does this mean that space has limits or is endless?

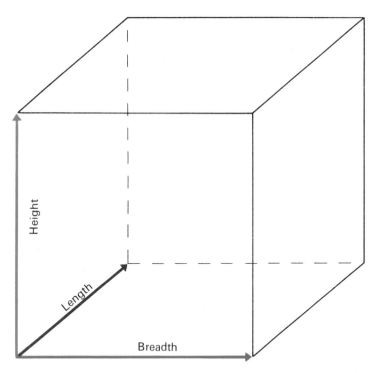

Height

Length

Breadth

We recognize three dimensions in space —length, breadth and height. Each dimension is at right angles to the other two.

experience ours spatially. This being is flat, as if it were drawn on a piece of paper, its world is limited to the surface of the paper, its concepts are determined by this one plane. A third dimension, which would be vertical in this flat world, for example height, would be as inconceivable to this being as a fourth, space-transcending dimension is in our spatially perceived world.

This flat being can only ever conceive of its world as a level plane, as a table-top (if its world is finite) or as endless (if it is infinite). We, however, want to see it not as level but as curved, like the surface of a giant sphere. We can do this because we have the capacity to perceive spatially. That is impossible for the flat being. It can only ever see its world as two-dimensionally level and flat, much as the ancients believed Earth to be.

If, proceeding from the concept (so familiar to us) of a huge sphere—Earth, say—we tell the flat being that the surface of its universe is not infinitely great, but measures a specific number of square metres (in the case of Earth it would be 510 million million square metres or 5,500 million million square miles), our flat being would imagine it limited in the same way that a table-top or disc is limited. It would ask what comes after the end of this surface, and what lies beyond the limit— just as men used to ask what existed beyond the edge of the world.

Our answer has to be that the surface has no end or limit. One could move as far as one liked in any direction and never reach the end. This seems contradictory to the flat being: if the surface has a finite size, then it must have an edge and must be bordered by something.

But the anomaly is only apparent and comes from the restricted nature of the being's powers of imagina-

reasons why it cannot be so. If we then ask what comes *after* space, and what forms the border of space, his answer will be that space has no end and no border. But that seems to be a contradiction. If space is finite, must it then not also have an end?

Our physicist would say not. The contradiction is only apparent and comes from the limitations of our powers of imagination. Space, which we experience as three-dimensional (having height, breadth and length), is in reality something different, higher, four-dimensional. To the three dimensions which we see, we should add a fourth "which transcends space". Our space has warped itself into this fourth dimension and closed itself off. Thus it has no limits but, at the same time, is still not infinite. This is difficult to understand.

The fourth dimension

An analogy might help. Let us imagine a being which experiences its world as a flat surface, just as we tion. The surface which it sees and experiences two-dimensionally, is in reality something different and three-dimensional. The plane of its universe has warped into this third dimension (as we know, the surface of a sphere) and has closed itself off. Thus it is endless and limitless, and yet not infinite.

This corresponds with our conversation with the physicist. It shows that a space which is unlimited but still not infinite is *conceivable* if it is warped into a fourth dimension and is closed in on itself. The fact that this space is not easily imagined is no argument against the possibility that it exists.

Our flat being, in spite of its limited powers of imagination, could still discover that its world is not two- but three-dimensional. It could establish, for example, that with very large triangles, the sum of the angles can be more than 180 degrees, as is the case with triangles drawn on a sphere. So our flat being would be forced to the conclusion that the surface of its world is not level but curved, for the sum of the angles in plane geometry is always exactly 180 degrees. Perhaps it could then put its ideas to the test and establish whether, if one marches long enough in the same direction, one eventually returns to the starting-point. We know that this is indeed the case.

In the same way there are indications that the four-dimensional nature of space is not merely mathematical but factual reality. The search is already under way for worlds which are so far away that they could be described as being on the "other side" of space. Since there is a limit to the observable universe, and the distant galaxies are receding at the speed of light, light waves do not get through to us over such great distances. The search has been made for very distant

sources of radio emission and it is believed that twenty-six have actually been found.

The view that space is four-dimensional is not only physically and mathematically flawless but it is also the only conceivable answer which satisfies the question of whether space is limited or infinite.

So space is probably "curved" not "flat", and figures have even been given for the radius of curvature (in the fourth dimension) of the universe. Even the hypothetical flat being could have calculated the radius of its curved world from the deviations in the sums of the angles of the spherical triangles.

The radius of curvature of space is calculated to be 30,000 trillion (that is 3 with 22 noughts) kilometres (18,600 trillion miles). The volume of space can then be calculated as 27×10^{67} cubic kilometres ($6 \cdot 5 \times 10^{27}$ cubic miles).

Space, time and matter

Let us now turn to a consideration of the relationships between space, time and matter. According to

The surface of a sphere is a surface curved in space, that is in the third dimension. Its central point is not on it but in the space surrounded by it. It has a definite size but no limits.

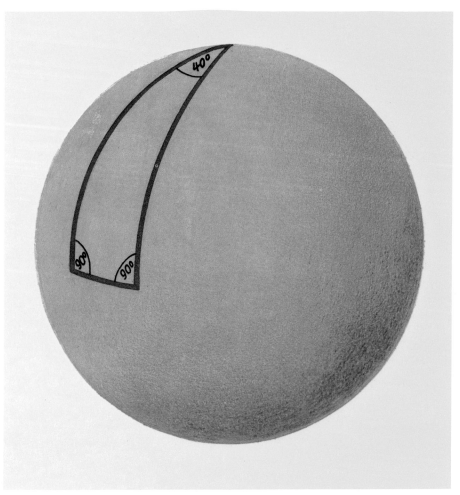

The sum of the angles of a triangle on a sphere is always more than 180 degrees.

physicists, space, time and matter are inseparably interwoven so none can exist without the other two. Thus no change can involve one without the other two being affected.

It is perfectly clear that space is the prerequisite for the existence of matter. We know that only a minute fraction of the space occupied by an atom is filled by matter, but where the atom occurs it fills the space completely and leaves no room for anything else.

The relationship between matter and time is similar, if not quite so obvious. Matter is understood to be a manifestation of oscillations and so includes time. Each oscillation requires time and can only exist in time. Matter is thus impossible without time and space and up to this

point our views are in accordance with those of the physicists.

The relationship of time and space to matter, on the other hand, is different. According to our ideas, space could be completely empty. It could exist without matter, independently, that is it could exist in the absolute sense. Time would continue to pass, also independently, even if nothing at all were happening. It too could exist without matter in an absolute sense.

Both these views are deceptive however. Admittedly it is difficult to imagine in exactly what way space and time are interdependent and are connected with matter, but they undoubtedly are. The theory of relativity indicates that space and time change for a body which is moving very fast. Space contracts for it and time slows down for it. Strictly speaking, therefore, every body in the universe has its own space and time. Space and time exist only in connection with matter, they are impossible without it and are not absolute. The fact of these inter-relationships is indisputable, because certain natural phenomena are known that cannot be explained in any other way. Thus modern science explains that space, time and matter are three inseparable, mutually dependent phenomena. This concept which may be difficult to appreciate helps us considerably in our reflections. This interrelationship means that everything we observe in one of these manifestations must also hold true for the other two and it enables us to find solutions to otherwise insoluble problems.

Given these circumstances, the thought occurs to us that the "recession" of the spiral galaxies, described in Chapter 9, cannot be without effect on space itself, for we are dealing with enormous quantities of matter and extremely high velocities. It is generally accepted today that this recession is not actually a movement of the spiral galaxies out into the existing but still empty (that is absolute) reaches of space, but rather is an "expansion" of space itself. In other words space only comes into existence with the advance of matter.

Applying this to our hypothetical flat being, that would mean that the surface of its world would simply be stretching like the surface of a balloon which is being blown up. Here too all points on the surface recede from each other in all directions. To be precise, they move away from each other more quickly if the intervals between them are greater. Furthermore, at each of these points, one has the impression of being at

the centre of this movement of flight.

This is precisely how one has to try to picture the increase in the radius which lies in the fourth dimension, and thus the volume of space, in which all the points are moving away from each other, their speeds of recession corresponding directly to the distances between them.

This image, which follows virtually of necessity from physical realities, avoids two important difficulties which are encountered if the "big bang" theory of the origin of the universe is accepted.

The first of these is the big bang itself which would be just *too* big to be acceptable even in cosmic terms. It is not the matter in space but space itself which is expanding, allowing all the galaxies to recede uniformly from each other without the necessity of an original massive explosion.

The second difficulty is that, if we adopt the big bang theory, we would find ourselves at the centre of the movement of the galaxies and thus at the centre of space. In four-dimensional space however, there

Space and time are inseparably bound to matter, just as the front and back of a piece of paper are to the piece of paper.

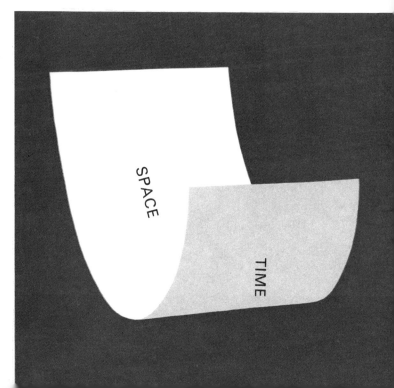

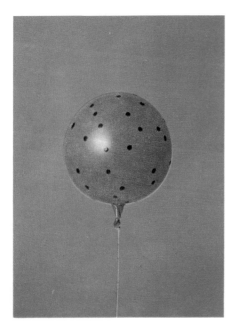
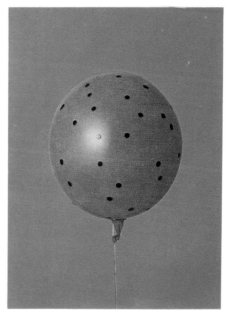

cannot be such a central point within the three dimensions which we perceive. Nor can there be a centre in the plane of the flat being, for this point—the centre of the sphere—does not lie on the plane itself but in the third dimension, that is in space. In addition the centre of the universe does not lie in three-dimensional space but in the fourth dimension. Consequently, one must be wary of any theory which tries to convince us of a central point in three-dimensional space.

Accordingly, the figure of 30,000 trillion kilometres (18,600 trillion miles) that we gave for the radius of the universe is only the present value, and can be understood to be constantly increasing. It is assumed that it is increasing at such a rate that three-dimensional space is expanding in all directions at the speed of light (300,000 kilometres or 186,000 miles per second). This means that the radius of the cosmos is considered to be increasing in size at the speed of light and that its precise radius would be 30,000 trillion kilometres (18,600 trillion miles) in 10,000 million years.

In this way we have defused the big bang theory to some extent, even if the question of how we are to see the origin and beginning of creation is still open.

Now the problem is not to establish where the first great primeval star, or the energy for the big bang, came from. Instead we must ask more specifically, where matter comes from, what causes the expansion of space and, since space and matter are intimately connected, whether these two questions are not perhaps the same.

Before we examine the question of how big space is, it is important that we appreciate the vast scale of the universe. Let us suppose we look at the sky on a clear moonless night, unhindered by street or artificial lighting. We should see the Milky Way, which Galileo rightly concluded was a vast number of stars. But well away from the Milky Way, the stars appear to be much less plentiful. In fact, in the whole northern and southern hemispheres only about 6,500 stars can be seen with the naked eye.

Consider now an area of the dark

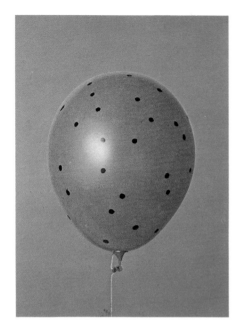 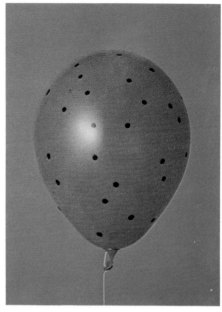

On the surface of an expanding sphere, all points recede from one another.

sky, rather smaller than that covered by the full Moon, in which just one star is visible with the naked eye. If we were to photograph this small area through a telescope using lengthy timed exposures, we should find that this area is filled with at least 3,000 stars and gaseous nebulae. The same result would be obtained by photographing any other area of the night sky which appears, to our eyes, to contain very few stars. Even such photographic techniques are, however, limited by our atmosphere and by technical considerations, hence the actual number of stars in our universe is far greater than we could have imagined by merely looking at the night sky from Earth.

When we consider our own galaxy, the Milky Way, we find that our Sun is only one of 100,000 million stars. Earlier this century, it was thought that the Sun was at the centre of the galaxy, but we now know that it lies about half-way between the centre and the outer rim of the galaxy. Even a galaxy, however, is not the largest unit in the universe, in spite of its enormous size. The majority of galaxies form clusters ranging from two or three to several thousand in number. The Milky Way and Andromeda are both members of a group of about twenty galaxies.

We might imagine that, because a galaxy contains such a large number of stars, the number of galaxies in the universe would be relatively small. But this would be a false assumption. In fact, in 1924, the American astronomer Hubble estimated that within a distance of 500 million light years from planet Earth there are about 100 million galaxies and additionally that there are many large and many small clusters of galaxies.

We have already seen that the average distribution of stars in space is relatively sparse. Clearly such vast numbers of stars as we know to be in existence can only be thinly distributed through an enormous universe. This prompts us to ask ourselves whether space is finite or infinite. In other words, does space go on for ever or is there perhaps some kind of boundary or limit to our space?

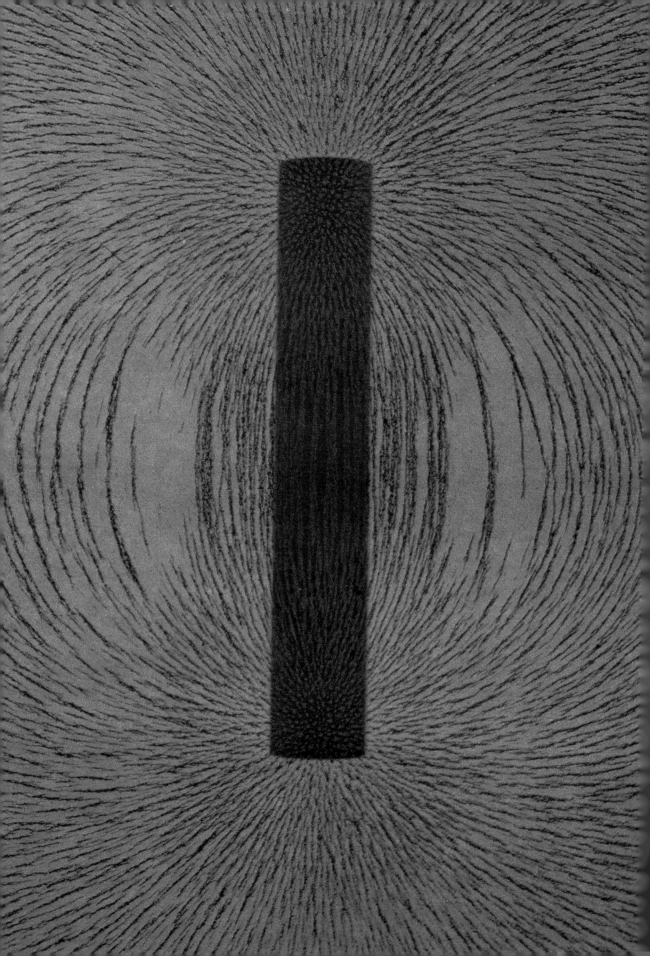

CHAPTER 11

MATTER AND ENERGY

The origin of matter

Now we have reached the question of the origin of matter which is the most severe test of any cosmogony.

Matter is anything that can be weighed, however heavy or light. Matter can exist in a solid, liquid or gaseous state. By changing its atomic structure or its chemical composition it can be transformed into a multiplicity of materials, but it can *never* arise from nothing, nor can it disappear into nothing. That is one of the basic principles of physics.

Matter exists in the universe in the shape of stars, planets, asteroids, moons, comets, meteorites, debris, dust, cosmic nebulae and interstellar matter. Its total quantity, as we have already suggested, has been estimated at 7×10^{48} tons, and this quantity is considered to be constant, precisely because no atom can be created from nothing or disappear into nothing. However, in modern physics this principle has been enlarged. It was Albert Einstein who discovered that matter and energy are manifestations of the same thing, and are interchangeable.

Energy

Energy is anything that performs or can perform work. It can occur in the form of latent energy, as in a taut spring or a raised weight. It can be active, as in the violence of an explosion or latent in matter, as in flowing water. It can also be distant from matter, as in heat or light radiation. Energy can occur in chemical, electrical, magnetic, thermal and other forms, and can be transformed from any one form into another. But like matter, it can never be created from nothing nor disappear into nothing. This also is a basic principle of physics. This is the prime reason why physicists reject out of hand the idea of a *perpetuum mobile* or perpetual machine, that is a machine which will perform without any input of energy. A genuine perpetual machine would create energy from nothing and so such a thing is impossible.

Energy is present in the universe primarily in the form of the light and heat radiation of the stars, in cosmic radiation and radio emission. It is also present in the tremendous pressures and temperatures inside the stars and in the magnetic, electrical and gravitational fields that extend throughout space. It occurs too in the rotational and orbiting movements of the celestial bodies.

Its quantity is considered to be fixed and constant, according to the Law of the Conservation of Energy of classical physics, since no quantum of light can be created from nothing nor can it disappear into nothing.

The lines of force of a magnet illustrate the presence of energy in a magnetic field. They show the direction of the magnetic force.

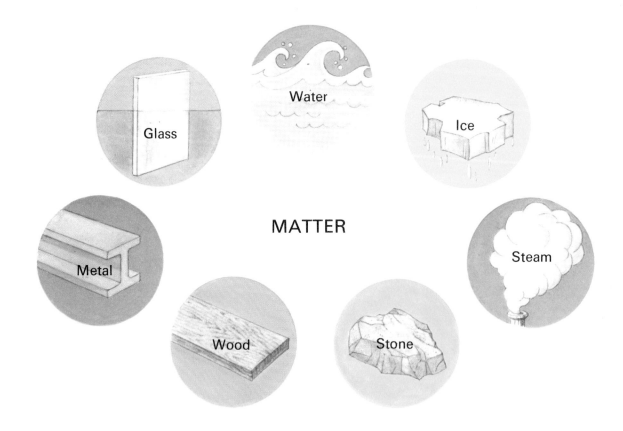

MATTER

Matter and energy

In modern physics, however, the two principles of the conservation of matter and energy have been joined in a single principle. It is known that matter can be transformed into energy and vice versa, that it is not the quantity of matter and the quantity of energy in themselves which are constant, but their sum-total. As a result, new energy can appear in the universe, as indeed happens in the stars, if a corresponding amount of matter disappears, and new matter can also appear if energy disappears.

Even if we do not know more about the nature of energy and matter, this item of knowledge is sufficient to bring us face to face with an apparently insuperable contradiction.

If we must accept unconditionally that the sum-total of matter and

energy is constant and unchanging, then this quantity can never have been *created* because that would represent the most fundamental change possible. It must have existed from eternity. Then it would appear however, that the universe, which must be formed in some shape by a sum of matter plus energy, can itself not have been created 10,000 million years ago but must also have existed from eternity. It was this anomaly that gave rise to the view expressed in Chapter 1, that the universe renews itself in an eternal cycle in which the star-matter which has been transformed into energy, is converted back into matter and begins life as a star again. We saw, however, that this theory is not acceptable. Added to that, all the evidence which points to the beginning 10,000 million years ago, definitely excludes the possibility of such a cycle.

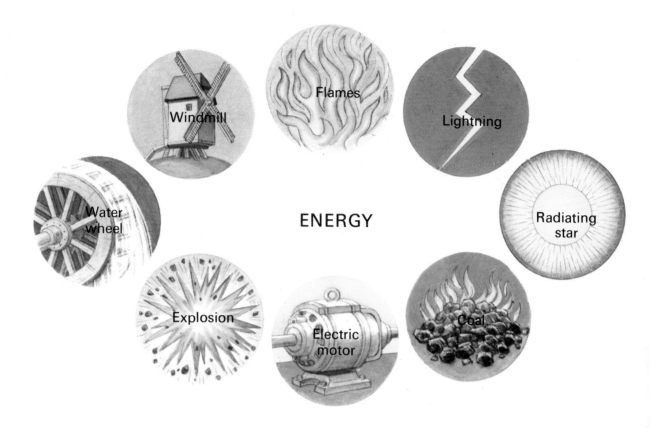

ENERGY

Windmill

Flames

Lightning

Water wheel

Radiating star

Explosion

Electric motor

Coal

The idea we discussed in Chapter 9 —that matter has always existed in the form of rarefied interstellar matter which only began to condense into stars 10,000 million years ago— is completely nullified by the recession of the spiral galaxies, which demands quite the opposite, namely an over-concentrated, hyper-dense state at the beginning of creation.

Consequently, the only possibility that cannot be completely excluded must be the "great star" which allegedly formed for a moment on the collapse of a previous universe and then expanded to form the cosmos. If this idea is pursued back into eternity, the universe will be an endless progression of collapse, great star, expansion and collapse, in which every collapse would have to occur with absolute precision in space and time. If this series of events was unlikely in the case of only one collapse, then the eternal repetition of the process could lead eventually only to total chaos, and certainly not to the creation of a primeval star in which all existing matter is concentrated at one moment in time and one point in space. Since this solution is also impossible we are left with the conclusion that the universe, and thus the matter of which it is composed, was created, or at least began to be created, 10,000 million years ago.

What was this matter created from. Was it really created from nothing, after all? How can this contradiction be resolved? One possibility remains, which was indicated by the German physicist Pascual Jordan.

Latent energy

The sum of matter plus energy remains constant because that is unalterable. Nevertheless, this sum-

Energy can appear in a variety of forms but cannot be created from nothing.

total includes a negative term, that is the energy of the gravitational field. In order to see what conclusions this can lead to we must digress.

We know that there is a certain amount of energy present in a coiled spring and, by inducing tension in the spring, it is possible to charge it with a certain quantity of energy which can be used to drive a clockwork motor. While the spring is driving the motor, the tension diminishes in proportion to the energy which is used and eventually disappears. The tension of the spring is thus the form in which the energy is stored. Tensions in steel are synonymous with latent energy. It

need not be steel or a similar solid body, for energy is present also in the steam of a boiler under pressure.

Energy need not be restricted to mechanical tension or gaseous pressures, it can also be magnetic. Thus we meet again a phenomenon that we have already used as an analogy, one that is very familiar to us but one which we find difficulty in understanding although we can appreciate its effects. The forces which a magnet exerts at its poles, or as we say, in its "magnetic field", are also effective in the vacuum of space. These forces are independent of materials, although it is difficult to understand precisely what happens. It must be so because every magnet attracts

Energy is present in a wound-up watch spring. The energy can be used to drive the watch.

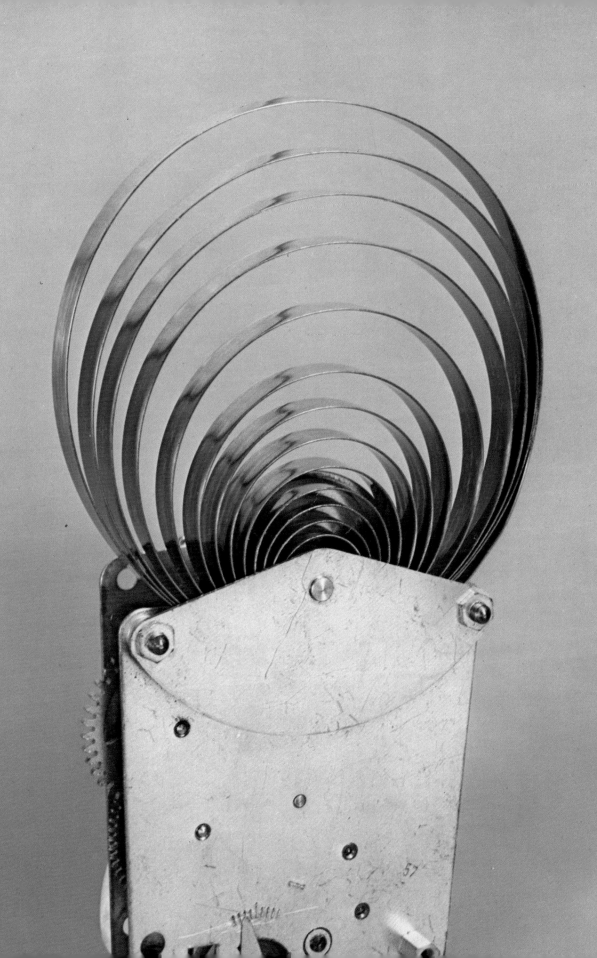

iron—even across a vacuum.

To take an analogy, the magnetic fields are depicted by "lines of force" which represent the energy at work in the areas surrounding the magnet whether it is large or small. In reality there is nothing there, only the forces, the direction of which are indicated by the lines. The forces that exist in the field of a magnet mean latent energy prevails there, just like the tension in the watch-spring or the pressure in the steam. So it is possible to have latent energy in a vacuum.

If a magnetic field is created by using an electro-magnet, a specific amount of electrical energy must be expended to build up the field. Once the field exists, a minimal current only is needed to feed the electro-magnet (this current has no effect on the field). If the magnetic field is cancelled by switching off the electric current, the field gives back the energy expended in building it up, in the form of a high-tension electrical impulse, and a spark is generated at the switch. This is because the energy present in the magnetic field cannot simply disappear, it has to exhaust itself in some way. This phenomenon is exploited in every internal-combustion engine to generate the spark in the sparking-plugs.

Energy is present in every type of "field", in the physical sense of the word. Thus every "field" can be seen as a state of tension in space, and these fields exist everywhere where invisible forces—such as the forces of attraction and repulsion—are at work.

The space round every celestial body is a physical force-field, because the attraction of mass, that is the gravity of the body, is at work within it. It affects and attracts everything that comes into its sphere of influence. The weight of a body is ultimately no more than this force of attraction. This gravitational field contains energy, and it is this which enables us to resolve the contradiction mentioned above. We exploit this energy when we use weights to drive a clock. When the weight is raised, energy is implanted in the gravitational field of Earth and the weight discharges this energy by slowly sinking down.

Just how great the tensions are that prevail in this gravitational field can be seen from the fact that to replace the force with which Earth keeps the Moon in position in space, a cable of best steel 600 kilometres (373 miles) in diameter would be required. We are concerned in this respect with a force of attraction equivalent to 20,000 billion tons which Earth exerts only upon the Moon, which after all occupies only a minute fraction of the space round Earth.

The energy of a gravitational field is, however, distinctly different from the energy found in other types of force-field. The gravitational field of a quantity of matter is greater, and thus the gravity-field energy is also greater the more densely it is concentrated. To weaken a gravitational field, it is necessary to distribute the matter which causes the field in space. To dissolve it completely, the matter would have to be distributed throughout space. That can only be done in opposition to the mass-attraction exerted by the matter, that is energy must be applied—just as in the lifting of weights.

The case with a gravitational field is exactly the opposite of the other examples. If one destroys a magnetic field it discharges energy, but if one wishes to dissolve a gravitational field, one must put energy into it. A logical step from this is that one can expect the building up or strengthening of a gravitational field not to consume energy but to release it. If a magnetic field represents latent energy, a gravitational field means negative energy, in other words an "energy-hole" that must be filled if the field is to disappear.

We can best clarify this point by means of a simple analogy. First, let us imagine a smooth sand surface which represents the energy-level zero. Matter, or positive energy, which we can equate are represented in our image by a mound of sand, and negative energy, in other words our "energy-hole", by a hole in the sand.

If we want to represent matter, we must bear in mind that there is no mass without gravity and no matter without its accompanying gravity-field with its negative energy. We must build a pile of sand on the surface. Also, to represent the gravity-field, it is necessary to excavate a trench in the sand round the mound.

If the sand that has to be excavated

Energy is released from the pressure of steam. An exploding steam boiler can do great damage.

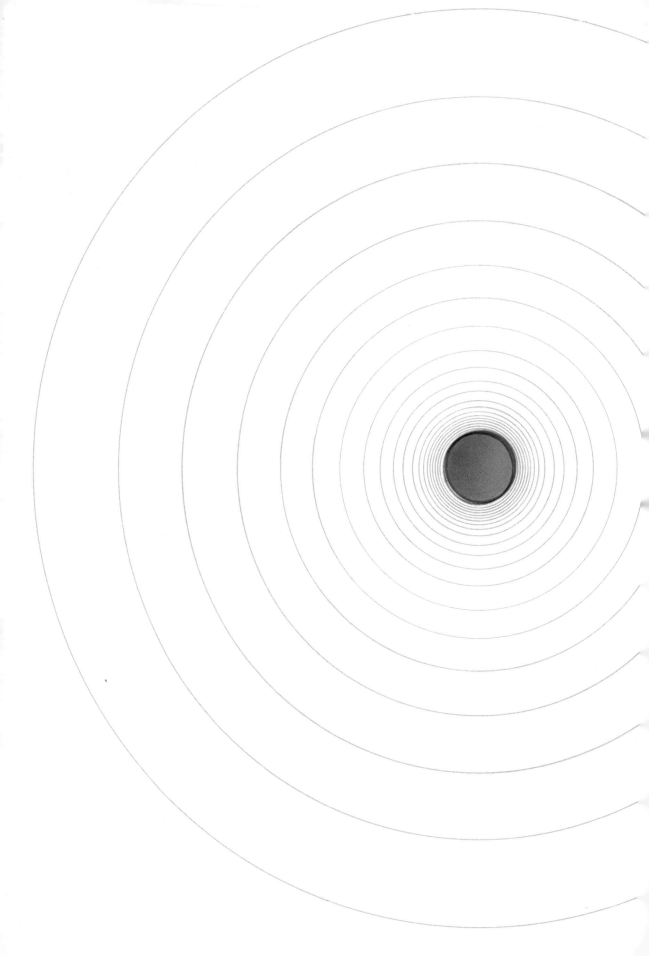

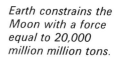

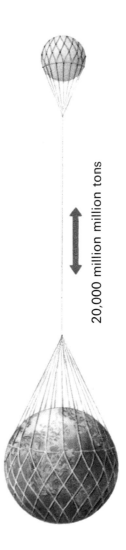

20,000 million million tons

is equal to the sand needed for the mound, we could create matter with its concomitant gravitational field, without having to introduce sand from outside. We could create it from the energy-level zero, that is the original level sand surface, because the sum of the matter plus the negative gravity-field energy would be equal to zero, just as before we constructed the mound and dug the trench.

That means that the creation of matter from nothing is conceivable, if the "energy-hole" connected with the gravity-field is as large as the matter created, in other words if the matter being created is accompanied

The gravitational field of a celestial body represented by lines of force. This is modelled on the lines of force of a magnetic field.

111

by its own counterbalance in the shape of its negative gravity-field energy.

If a possibility of fulfilling this condition exists, a key to the solution of our contradictory question will have been found. Even if one proceeds from nothing—the level surface of the sand—matter can be created in this particular instance without the sum-total of matter plus energy being changed, and without the basic precondition being transgressed, for the sum of matter and energy is zero as before. There are in fact states of matter in which this condition is fulfilled.

The Theory of Relativity which was developed by Albert Einstein had far-reaching effects on the fields of physics, astronomy and cosmo-logy. We shall examine this subject briefly as some of its implications are fundamental to our study of the link between matter and energy.

The starting-point for Einstein's theory was the experimental result that the speed of light is always constant, independent of the speed of the observer. This led on to the result that no object could have a speed equal to or greater than the speed of light. In fact, Einstein's formula predicts that as an object's speed increases, its mass increases and therefore its energy increases. If an object were to reach the speed of light, it would require an infinite amount of energy and this is clearly impossible. This upper limit to the speed of any vehicle indicates to us why interstellar space travel is such

If a level surface of sand represents energy level zero, then matter is a pile of sand surrounded by a trench—its gravitational field with its negative energy charge.

a remote possibility. It would take us at least four years to reach the nearest star to our Sun (if we could travel at the speed of light).

Before the Theory of Relativity was developed it was assumed that mass, length and velocity were independent quantities. This was certainly in agreement with our everyday experience. However, Einstein postulated that this was not true for speeds which are a considerable percentage of the speed of light. For example, let us see what relativity predicts for a rod which is moving with 90 per cent of the speed of light. At this speed its mass is more than double its mass at rest, its normal length is about halved and a clock on the rod would slow down. An observer travelling on

the rod would observe none of these strange effects—they could only be seen by a stationary observer.

The results of relativity are difficult to believe because their effects on our everyday experiences are too small to be measured. However, scientific experiments have been carried out and have verified the predictions of relativity.

Einstein reasoned that since motion involves energy and since mass increases with motion, it follows that energy has mass. He then developed a fundamental equation which established the link between mass and energy. This equation tells us that the energy locked up in matter is equal to mass times the square of the speed of light. This equation also tells us that if only a small amount of matter could be converted completely into energy, a vast amount of energy could be released. This method of energy release is the principle behind the atomic and hydrogen bombs. The production of energy by stars is also based on the same principle. The basic process is the combination of hydrogen atoms to form helium atoms with a slight loss of mass. The vast amounts of energy which are produced by this loss of mass according to Einstein's equation, are radiated into space and, in the case of our Sun, supply energy to us on Earth.

The implications of relativity which we have just discussed have been verified by scientific experiments. However, Einstein attempted to extend the Theory of Relativity to include and explain the effects of gravity. Just as we have already mentioned that mass, length and velocity are in fact related quantities, Einstein postulated that space and time are related. This concept is much more difficult to verify experimentally.

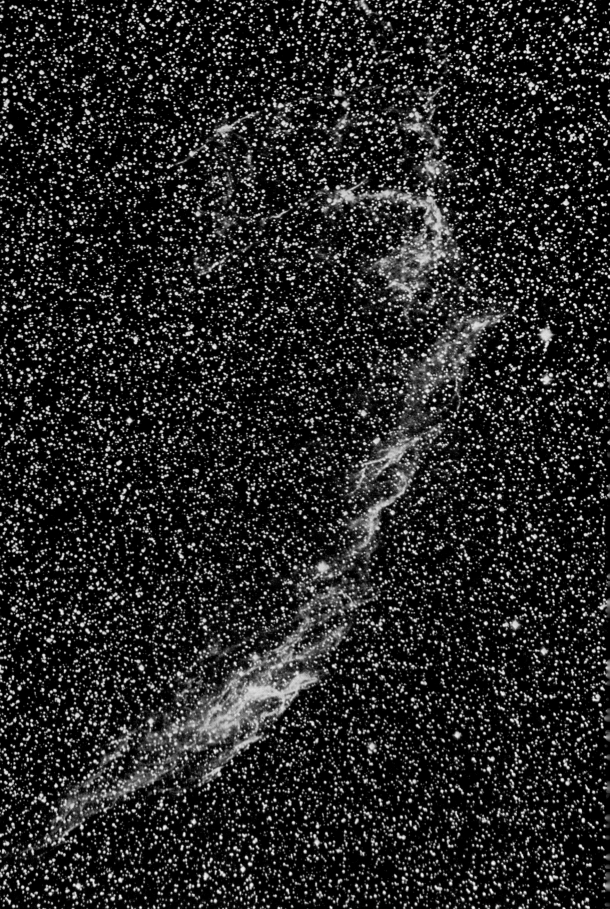

CHAPTER 12

COSMOGONY

If all the threads of our arguments about time, space and matter are drawn together, we can try to imagine the universe 10,000 million years ago, and attempt to understand what existed then. We shall also try to show what might have happened then and how the universe has evolved to its present state. Although some statements may appear difficult to understand, the conclusions that follow from them seem very reasonable, indeed they are the only ones which satisfy the facts which are known at present.

Time, space and matter

In Chapter 10 we considered that space was of finite size and was expanding at a constant rate. If we go back in time we conclude that space was smaller. If we use a two-dimensional analogy it was smaller, like the surface of a child's balloon which has been deflated. This means that all the galaxies were closer together than they are at present, just as the points on the surface of the balloon became closer together as it was deflated. This is the exact opposite of the actual observed recession of the galaxies.

How far back in time is this process feasible? Does not the tremendous mass of the spiral galaxies, some 7×10^{48} tons of matter, prescribe a limit to the shrinking of space as they draw closer together? We established in Chapter 10, that time, space and matter are inseparably bound together. In other words, if there is no space there is no matter, or in another way, there is less matter if there is less space.

Space can only be reduced if the matter also diminishes. This is true not only when the process of reduction is at an advanced stage, for example towards the beginning of the universe, but also universally and in every case. The modern view is that the average density of matter in space is constant, because of the intimate connections between space and matter. It has been estimated to occur at the rate of one gram per 40 million million cubic kilometres (0·035 ounce per 10 million million cubic miles), that is a cube of space the sides of which are all 34,000 kilometres (21,000 miles) long. This means that any change in space must lead to a corresponding change in the amount of matter. Space and matter therefore stand in a fixed relationship of balance. This steady state theory has been developed particularly by the English mathematician and astrophysicist Fred Hoyle.

Can the quantity of matter be reduced when space is reduced? In Chapter 11, we indicated that it cannot disappear without trace into nothing.

If matter is to disappear it must be

The Veil nebula in Cygnus is perhaps the result of a supernova explosion thousands of years ago—an event from which (according to one hypothesis) new matter is formed.

transformed into energy, and the question then is what happens to this energy? If matter disappears the gravitational field caused by it must also disappear. We discussed earlier the fact that in order to dissolve a gravitational field energy must be applied. Thus energy is required if the gravitational field associated with matter is to be removed and matter is to disappear.

Towards the end of Chapter 11 we indicated that a state of matter exists in which the "energy-hole" associated with the gravitational field is the same size as the matter, now transformed into energy from which it came. If we return to our analogy, there is a state in which the hole dug in the level surface of sand represents the gravitational field, and it is as great as the mound of sand which was piled up to represent the amount of matter from which the gravitational field is derived. If this possibility is accepted as a realistic appraisal of the conditions, the presence of matter sets no limit to the reduction in the size of space. The matter that must disappear as space is reduced is always precisely what is necessary to dissolve, in the form of energy, the gravitational field which must disappear with it.

If the radius of the universe, and thus its volume, approaches the value zero, then the amount of matter and the negative energy of the gravitational field also approach zero. The mound of sand in our analogy has become smaller, but so also has the hole in the sand.

Now we are equipped to go back some 10,000 million years to the point in time when the radius of the universe must have been zero, as can be seen from the rate of expansion of space and the distance of the spiral galaxies given in Chapter 9. When the radius of the universe is zero, so is the volume of space re-

The Hantel nebula in Vulpecula, a planetary nebula, originated in an exploding star which hurled a large quantity of matter into space.

duced to zero. *There is no more space.* The child's balloon has been deflated to such an extent that it has disappeared into nothing.

If space is non-existent, all matter must have disappeared too. The pile of sand we made and the hole we dug have disappeared. *There is no more matter or energy.* The levelled surface of the sand means precisely that the energy level is zero.

Since, without space and matter there can be no time, we stand at the beginning of time. Thus the concept "before" cannot exist.

These ideas are very difficult to appreciate and it is very hard to consider a state where absolutely nothing exists—that is there is no space, matter or time. Nevertheless, we are forced to this conclusion if we proceed from the assumption that the universe really did come into existence at some point in time and did not simply develop from some previous state.

If anything at all existed at the beginning of the universe, then according to our conclusions it must have been something completely independent of time, space and matter, that is something completely different, an "absolute value" that cannot be understood in terms of the concepts we are familiar with in the universe around us. It cannot possibly be understood in terms of what we know, for all our ideas are based on time, space and matter. We only understand and experience the world around us because it lies within these dimensions. We have arrived at the beginning of all things, and can now attempt to follow through the formational processes of our universe.

Formation of the universe

In the beginning there was absolute nothingness.

The concept of an absolute void is impossible for us to appreciate fully because it is completely outside our experience. There was no space to act as the stage for the events we witness today. There was no primeval abyss in which the universe could have originated, no yawning emptiness, because that would still have been space.

There was no time, in which the birth of the universe could have taken place. Neither was there a "before" in which it could have been prepared and no process out of which it could have developed.

Matter did not exist, that is the material out of which the universe is made, was not present even in an unformed, chaotic state from which it could have developed to the state we witness today. There was no physical energy, in any form which could have affected any change.

The beginning consists of the "fact" that, around 10,000 million years ago, space, time and matter began to form together in one, inseparably interwoven process.

In the creation of matter from its own negative gravity-field energy, however, there existed one limitation, as mentioned at the end of Chapter 11. It can only be formed in the densest concentration, and in minimum quantity which is considerable even by cosmic standards. The creation of neutrons or hydrogen atoms, for example—that is interstellar matter—would consequently not have been possible under what we know of the conditions which then obtained. Neutrons would, admittedly, correspond to these conditions with respect to density, but not by a long way with regard to quantity.

So Pascual Jordan concluded that matter today originates in the form of "supernovae", in which these conditions would be fulfilled.

Supernova

A supernova is a star which, like the nova described in Chapter 8, appears in the sky in a mighty outburst of energy and light. This phenomenon is one of the most awesome events that we know in the universe. It is a thousand times more violent than a nova outburst, and is thus surely of a different nature. The major part of the matter in the star is hurled out into space, where it joins other interstellar matter. A supernova radiates in the first twenty-five days of its existence as much energy as our Sun radiates in one million years. After its sudden outburst the star reverts within two or three years to about a hundred times the Sun's brightness. A supernova is observed in the Milky Way every 200 or 300 years. However, the view is generally held today that a supernova represents a normal stage in the life of certain types of stars which have much greater masses than the Sun.

Space-field

An idea has been presented by Fred Hoyle, which suggests that apart from the gravitational field connected with matter, there is another more general "space-field" connected with space, that is that even space which is thought of as empty, actually represents a negative energy source. Thought of in another way, this would be an explanation for the inseparable relationship between space and matter. Accordingly, space as negative energy is bound to need matter as positive energy in order to exist or to be a reality.

If we transfer this concept to our image of the level surface of sand, the creation of a specific volume of space would mean that within a corresponding area of sand, the level of the sand would have to be lowered by a uniform amount to represent the general space-field. The requisite amount of sand would then have to be piled up in one or more places, if only for somewhere to put it, that is matter *must* then be created. Apart from that, as we have already seen, the sunken surface of the sand would still have to be excavated further in the vicinity of the pile or piles of sand to represent their individual gravitational fields. The bulk of the energy for the creation of matter would thus come from the general space-field and to a lesser

The Omega nebula in the Marksman consists of light and dark gas and dust masses as if it could also have originated in a supernova explosion and then become the birthplace of stars

extent from the gravitational field.

According to these ideas, the creation of matter is feasible at any time, even today, and in any, even the smallest, quantity. In fact, this must be so otherwise we could not explain the universal distribution of hydrogen atoms throughout the cosmos. So our universe was created when, at the beginning of time, the two complementary basic elements, matter and space emerged from nothing—as Heaven and Earth did in the Sumerian myth. Whereas in the Sumerian and all the other cosmogonies, including Genesis, the world was complete after its crea-

tion, in our cosmogony that is only the beginning. Time began with this process.

After 4,000 millionths of a second, so much space had been created that the concomitant negative energy demanded the creation of a neutron in compensation. After ten seconds, the radius of curvature of space was one million kilometres (625,000 miles), the volume of space was ten trillion cubic kilometres (2·5 trillion cubic miles) and the quantity of matter amounted to 2·5 tons. After ten minutes, the radius was 6,000 million kilometres (3,728 million miles), the volume was two quad-

in the past and arise still stars and suns and, with them, swarms of planets.

In this way our Sun was created 4,700 million years ago, to form, in the course of a few hundred million years, its solar system. That was when Earth and its Moon were born, to which an age of 4,500 million years has been ascribed.

Our universe is not complete; it is not a finished work. It is in the process of evolving just as on the first day. The same events are happening as on the day when it all began.

Meanwhile, time has reached the 10,000-million-year mark, the radius of curvature of space has grown to 30,000 trillion kilometres (18,642 trillion miles), the volume of the universe has reached 27×10^{67} cubic kilometres (6.75×10^{67} cubic miles) and the quantity of matter has increased to seven octillion tons. The process continues, on and on through the ages, and we stand within this overpowering cosmic process of creation and unfolding, to which we belong, and in which we have a specific role. The question which springs to mind is, why are we here?

In 1572, Tycho Brahe, the famous Danish astronomer, made careful observation of a brilliant new star which we now know to have been a supernova. This particular supernova was so bright that it far outshone Venus and was even visible in broad daylight. There have only been two other observations of supernovae in our own galaxy in the past 1,000 years. In 1604 Kepler noted the occurrence of one and in 1054 Chinese astronomers recorded the appearance of a supernova. The wreck of the Chinese supernova can still be seen as the gas cloud known to astronomers as the Crab nebula. It had been discovered that supernovae are also strong radio sources.

rillion cubic kilometres (0·5 quadrillion cubic miles) and the amount of matter 55,000 tons.

So it continued and still continues through the years, centuries, thousands, millions and thousands of millions of years—not merely at a uniform rate but increased with the cubed-power of time, so that after twice the time, eight times the volume and eight times the quantity of matter has been created.

The created matter collected and still collects in the spiral galaxies, there it concentrated and still concentrates to form the galactic nebulae, and from them there arose

CHAPTER 13

AND GOD SPOKE

If the cosmic processes which have been presented are accepted for the origin of the universe, the cosmos was formed not from existing matter in an already existing space at a point in time which is continuous, but it was created literally from nothing. It did not even require the application of physical forces or energies to start its formational process. If the entire universe, even today, is nothing in the physical sense, considering that everything within it is reciprocally balanced, then it needed no initial physical impulse. There was not even room for one.

Seen from the point of view of the physicist, everything could have begun of its own accord at any moment in time. There is no physical reason—indeed none is needed— why it should have begun 10,000 million years ago.

Whoever is satisfied with this explanation has received a final answer to the hidden difficulties behind the creation of the world, and thus need ask no more. Can we all be satisfied with this solution however?

Why?

Those who cannot believe that this mighty evolution, stretching over thousands of millions of years, developed and continues of its own accord; those who are not satisfied that all of this just accidentally began once, for no good reason; those who cannot relinquish the idea of a primary causality behind all of this, in spite of the flawless physical explanation—those people must seek this cause outside the realm of physical facts, for these are complete in themselves and allow of no such cause. This is the question of why and for what, which was discussed in Chapter 11, and its solution is not the job of the physicist.

In the last chapter we found that, if anything at all existed beforehand, it was independent of time, space and matter and not understandable in terms of the world we find around us. It could not be described in terms of the world we find around us. It could not be described in terms of these concepts, it could not be deduced from them, and it could not be understood in these terms. It was "metaphysical"—"supernatural" in the strictest sense of the word.

That means we have to refer to the concept of God, and so return finally, as with any cosmogony, to questions of theology. How are modern views to be reconciled with these?

They do not prevent us in the least from believing in God as the creator and supporter of the world. But they suggest to us that we should not

The Creation of the Heavens. *A mosaic at Monreale near Palermo, Sicily.*

God separates land and sea. God creates the birds and the fishes. Mosaic at Monreale near Palermo, Sicily.

have too primitive an image of Him, and that is surely a good thing.

Anyone who imagines the creation of the world in a naïve way, or dogmatically accepts the words of Genesis, will miss not only the actual course of events but also everything that Genesis was trying to express. He will think that the world was artificially introduced into empty space and empty time by the creation of matter or the shaping of matter into the universe. Space and time would thus have already existed, the empty stage for events, independent of creation and pre-dating it—presumably independent of God. We can fall into this mental trap if we do not take

account of the fact that empty space, and time devoid of event, are ultimately not "nothing", and that they must have been created exactly like matter in the creation out of nothing, the *creatio ex nihile*. The modern view compels us here to adopt an orderly way of looking at things, to take the creation out of nothing seriously, and to regard time and space as also created by God, since there can be no time and space without matter.

Perhaps today we would prefer to have Genesis begin with the words: "In the beginning God created time, space and matter, so that the world might evolve from them."

If we believe in God as the creator of time, He stands timeless before the beginning of time. Time is a manifestation of the natural world and does not apply to God. For Him there is no "before", no "now" and no "after". He is "from eternity to eternity".

If we believe in Him as the creator of space, then He existed before space. He is not to be conceived of in space. There is nowhere in natural space where He is to be found more or less than anywhere else. Space is a manifestation of the natural world. The limitations of space do not apply to God. He is neither inside nor outside space.

If we believe in Him as the creator of matter, He existed before matter. He cannot be understood in terms of matter and thus cannot be conceived of in the form of images, so for this reason one should make "no graven image" of Him.

The scientific attitude thus purifies our concept of God of unsuitable naïve images, and makes it deeper and more genuine. Genesis reverts to what it was originally intended to be—not a superficially scientific textbook but an overwhelming emphatic affirmation that there are not many gods but only one; that He created Heaven and Earth, everything visible and everything invisible and that, as we consider Him today—still creating it and supporting it. Creation is not complete, the world is not finished and men are not complete. Everything is still evolving, and this process will continue into the foreseeable future.

What is the goal? What is our role in this creation? Are we merely to live in it?

If we have been placed in this small part of the universe, with the ability to become consciously aware of it, to influence it and if only modestly to change it, is it then sufficient merely to use it, to subject it to our will, without considering whether there might not be a duty, a cosmic purpose attached to it?

We are born in the dawn of man's sojourn on Earth and can expect to know only a little about the universe. Albert Einstein has put it this way: "My religion consists of a humble admiration of the illimitable superior spirit who reveals himself in the slight details we are able to perceive with our frail and feeble minds. That deeply emotional conviction of the presence of a superior reasoning power, which is revealed in the incomprehensible universe, forms my idea of God."

ACKNOWLEDGMENTS

Cover: California Institute of Technology and Carnegie Institution of Washington. Front endpaper: A. Rudolph. Back endpaper: R. Bianchi, Berner Oberland (Hasliberg). 2: W. Ferchland. 6, 8 (above), 9: Zentrale Farbbildagentur (ZEFA). 8 (below left and right): H. Fay. 10 (2): Hale Observatories. 12: Staatsbibliothek Berlin. 14: ZEFA. 15, 16 (above): Staatsbibliothek Berlin. 16/17: ZEFA. 17 (right): Historia. 18/19: SCALA. 19 (right), 20: ZEFA. 21: H. Alexy. 22 (above), 22/23, 24: K. Bürgle. 25: Fay. 26 (left): Bürgle. 26/27: ZEFA. 28: USIS/NASA. 29: Fay. 30 (above): Deutsches Museum. 30 (below), 31, 32 (2), 33 (2), 34 (2), 35, 36 (2, above): Fay. 36 (centre left): USIS. 36 (below): Hale Observatories. 37: Fay. 38 (above): V-Dia Verlag. 38/39: Albrecht Brugger. 40: ZEFA. 41: L. Palnic. 42 (3), 43, 44, 45, 46, 46/47: Fay. 48, 51, 52: ZEFA. 53 (above) California Institute of Technology and Carnegie Institution of Washington. 53 (below): Hale Observatories. 54: Fay. 55: Hale. 56, 57: ZEFA. 58 (above), 58/59 (below): Fay. 59 (above): Deutsches Museum. 59 (below): Fay. 60: Bianchi. 61: Fay. 62: ZEFA. 63: JFS-Archiv. 64 (2), 65 (2), 66, 67; Fay. 68/69: ZEFA. 69 (right): Süddeutscher Verlag. 70/71: ZEFA. 72 (2), 73 (4): Kurt Krischke. 74: California Institute of Technology and Carnegie Institution of Washington. 75/76 (2), 77 (2), 78 (3), 79 (3), 80, 81: Fay. 82: California Institute of Technology and Carnegie Institution of Washington. 84: V-Dia. 85, 86 (left), 86/87 (below): Fay. 87 (right): Hale Observatories. 88 (above): Fay. 88 (below): California Institute of Technology and Carnegie Institution of Washington. 89: Bürgle. 90: California Institute of Technology and Carnegie Institution of Washington. 91 (above): Bürgle. 91 (below left): Deutsches Museum. 91 (below right), 92: Fay. 94: ZEFA. 95: Deutsches Museum. 96, 97, 98, 99: Fay. 100 (2), 101 (2): Alexy. 102: ZEFA. 104, 105: Fay. 106, 107: Alexy. 109: Süddeutscher Verlag. 110/111, 111, 112/113: Fay. 114: ZEFA. 116/117, 119: California Institute of Technology and Carnegie Institution of Washington. 120/121: Fay. 122, 124/125 (2): JFS-Archiv.

FURTHER READING

Alter, Dinsmore and others. 1969. *Pictorial Astronomy.* Thomas Y. Crowell (U.S.)

Beet, E. A. 1964. *The Solar System.* Blackie (U.K.)

Bergamini, D. 1969. *The Universe.* Time-Life Books (U.S.)

Bono, P. and Gatland, K. 1969. *Frontiers of Space.* Blandford (U.K.)

Bova, Ben. 1970. *In Quest of Quasars: An Introduction to Stars and Starlike Objects.* Crowell-Collier Press (U.S.)

Branley, F. M. 1964. *The Sun: Star Number One.* Crowell (U.S.)

Brown, P. L. 1971. *What Star is that?* Thames and Hudson (U.K.)

Brown, P. L. 1972. *Astronomy in Colour.* Blandford (U.K.)

De Galiana, T. 1968. *Concise Encyclopedia of Astronautics.* Collins (U.K.); Follett (U.S.)

Evans, D. S. 1970. *Teach Yourself Astronomy.* E.U.P. (U.K.)

Fisher, C. 1964. *Exploring the Heavens.* Crowell (U.S.)

Gallant, R. A. 1968. *Exploring Mars.* Doubleday (U.S.)

Kopul, Z. 1972. *Man and his Universe.* Rupert Hart-Davis (U.K.)

Leach, M. 1956. *The Beginning: Creation Myths Around the World.* Funk & Wagnalls (U.S.)

Muller, P. 1968. *Concise Encyclopedia of Astronomy.* Collins (U.K.); Follett (U.S.)

Rohr, H. 1972. *The Radiant Universe.* Warne (U.K.)

Silverberg, R. 1969. *The World of Space.* Meredith Press (U.S.)

Velikovsky, I. 1950. *Worlds in Collision.* Doubleday (U.S.)

von Braun, W. 1971. *Space Frontier.* Harcourt, Brace & Jovanovich (U.S.)